Dementia
or
Alzheimer's

A Daughter's Guide to Home Care
from the Early Signs and Onset of
Dementia through the Various
Alzerheimer Stages

Robin Gail

Here is a resource everyone with a loved one diagnosed with dementia should find extremely helpful. I have worked with many people affected with it for 10 years now, and can absolutely say everything in this book is accurate. This is a very touching story of the family's challenges in taking care of her mom in a home care setting from early onset to the end that is very hard to put down. She handled each "stage" with grace and sensitivity and portrays capably how it affected not only herself but the rest of the family's journey. Glenn L.

This is a great book for anyone caring for a loved one with dementia or Alzheimers. The author includes heartfelt examples of her journey, mistakes to avoid and helpful tips. I appreciate that there are tips for caring for my loved one as well as tips for self care. It really helps to have a real example to relate to so I know I am not alone. I'll be referencing this book often. Brandi J.

This book is a gem. Informative, heartfelt and human. Robin Gail draws upon her mother's inspirational story and shares valuable and practical advice so others can learn from their experience. This book can really help families help families who go through the challenges of caring for a loved one with Alzheimer's. Dr. E.V. Estacio, PhD, CPsychol, SFHEA

The author of this book writes a very heartwarming memoir about caring for her mother in the last stages of Alzheimer's. The book is meaningful and gives some wonderful suggestions to other family caregivers. I would recommend this book to anyone who has been or will be a caregiver of family members. N. Ann Lamphere, MSW, CSW

The information in this book is in no way intended to be medical advice or legal advice. It is intended to provide information that will inspire and uplift those who are caregivers. The author shares tips and solutions she used to solve many issues and problems that arose in the care of her mother. This is not a promise that these techniques will work for everyone. The author assumes no liability for use or abuse by anyone of the suggestions provided for caregiving in this book.

ISBN 978-0-9992476-4-8

Cover design by thefinalwrap.com

Contents

Acknowledgements

Heartfelt gratitude to my beautiful sister for her unselfish help and devotion to our mother. Thank you for understanding when my graciousness and patience was lacking.

Thank you to the love of my life for helping make this possible. Thank you for your unconditional love and help with Mom and for bringing me out of the depths of despair more than once as we cared for her in her struggle with this relentless disease. There are not enough words to describe what you mean to me.

Most importantly, I give thanks to God for His unending love and promises. My prayers were answered many times as we cared for Mom. When my faith was lacking, He reminded me to rely on Him and He would carry us through everything. He did.

"Sometimes you will never know the value of a moment until it becomes a memory."

Dr. Seuss

PREFACE

The word dementia has often been used to describe the mentally ill. After my mom started showing signs of extreme forgetfulness, I began research to learn what the cause of her memory problems could be. Countless articles listed forgetfulness as a symptom of dementia.

In my career as a court reporter, I am endlessly searching words in the dictionary. I researched the word dementia. Of the definitions listed, the one that disturbed me is insanity. No possible way my mother was insane.

How disheartening for someone who is concerned about the decline in their memory, to see insanity as a definition for dementia. Society has its own stigma of this disease too. If one develops lung cancer, their brain is outliving their body. If one develops cognitive decline, their body is outliving their brain. Is this insanity? I do not see it that way.

Upon further research, I discovered the word dementia is used in literature more often to express a cognitive decline. I watched my mother endure a slow cognitive decline, not insanity.

Dementia or Alzheimer's ?

This book is not advice regarding how to stave off dementia or how to live your life a certain way in order to escape the ravages of this disease. I have told my own personal story and experiences of caring for my beloved mother as she sank deeper and deeper into the abyss of this dreadful disease, a disease for which there is no cure. We will always hope and continue to pray research leads to treatment and ultimate prevention.

I write of my mother before she was stricken with dementia, how her life evolved to include this terrible disease and how she courageously coped with it. With no training at all in cognitive impairment and limited information regarding Mom's illness, my husband and I became her caregivers.

A number of people have told me I should write a book about our experience because we could possibly help others who find themselves in the midst of this journey. I attempted several times to begin this book shortly after my mother passed away, but it was too painful to relive it. I was not ready. So I started to document our experiences as I would recall them and put the slips of paper away for a later time.

As we traveled this journey with Mom, we found solutions to issues we would face on a daily basis. When a particular solution we tried would not work, we searched for other viable alternatives and often found one that would work. I have shared many of our findings here. We learned some of the ideas or suggestions in this book from speaking with and watching others. Much of the information is gleaned through conversations with other caregivers.

The challenges were relentless, but we knew it was critical to dwell on what Mom had left, not on what she was losing.

I had spent the last several years reading books and articles regarding Alzheimer's and how to care for one afflicted with this disease. Some of what we incorporated into our care for Mom we read. Much of what we incorporated was through trial and error. We learned countless ways to help her adjust, not only to her surroundings but to living with the disease she had.

After writing of some of our experiences, I provide nine chapters, beginning with my mother's journey and ending with celebrating the life of our loved ones. Some information may be redundant. Through taking care of Mom, we discovered the care while they are still able to live in their own home is much the same as the care of them when their disease progresses and they come to your home. Bear in mind, the symptoms of this disease could get worse quickly or take years to manifest themselves. This is different for each person. Early treatment for the symptoms of this disease may mean your loved one can stay independent for a longer time period.

When I say my mom or parent, I am speaking from our experience of taking care of my mother. Caregiving is a general term used, whether for your parent, your spouse, your sibling, your child or anyone else you may be caring for.

There are superb assisted living facilities as well as nursing homes available. However, the information found here is predominantly regarding care of your loved one in their home or in your home, as this is our personal experience.

When my family first understood we were embarking on this journey with Mom, I started intense research to learn how we could best help her. I spent many hours reading information about this abhorrent disease and asking questions of knowledgeable people.

Much of what I learned through research and applied in the care of Mom is shared in these pages. I provide this information, not as a professional in any capacity, but because I believe we have an insider's view of what happens to loved ones as they are in the throes of this demeaning disease. There is no how-to book or rule book that will prepare someone for the role of caregiver. We found the best way to learn was through other caregivers and their experiences. This writing is for informational purposes only, not intended to be medical advice or legal advice.

Please keep in mind, every experience as a caregiver is different. You must expect the unexpected. Throughout my research and speaking with others in this role, I found caregiving is relatively the same, no matter what the disease is. Again, I share our own personal experience with our mother. There are limited books regarding personal experiences of caregivers. It is my hope the information written here provides help and assistance for those who find themselves in the position of caregiver, as we did.

There are a number of medications on the market today that will not cure dementia or Alzheimer's, but they may improve memory and confusion by restoring the balance of certain substances in the brain. The ability to perform normal daily tasks may also be improved with some medications. Mom's ability improved dramatically after being prescribed Namenda.

<u>Dementia or Alzheimer's ?</u>

Information on these medications, called cholinesterase inhibitors, is plentiful on-line. Vitamin E is sometimes prescribed in higher amounts to combat cognitive changes in the brain. Discuss medication options with a physician. Before beginning any new medications for dementia, inform your physician of all medications your loved one is currently taking.

Many people have the opinion it is advantageous to have only one physician in charge of a person's care after the diagnosis of dementia. It may result in less confusion for all involved.

I have read in numerous articles and found that scientists agree, Alzheimer's may be caused by a combination of genetics and environmental factors. We are all aware proper diet and nutrition, staying physically fit and healthy daily habits help prevent some of the atrocious diseases that befall us.

While I am not a big believer in the old adage time heals all things, nor do I necessarily hold a belief in closure, I am certain time allows us to better cope and accept our losses in a different way. I know my life will not be the same without my mother in it, but great comfort comes in knowing she is not confused and lost anymore, she is at peace.

During the latter part of Mom's illness, we found a piece of paper in her Bible with a statement written in her own handwriting.

"To be absent from the body is to be in the presence of the Lord."

I know where she is. She does live on, in me and my siblings, in her grandchildren and great-grandchildren. The quote we found in her Bible is inscribed on her headstone.

Dementia or Alzheimer's ?

1 HER JOURNEY

My mother, Helen, was born November 10, 1931, in Emberson, Texas. She was one of four daughters born to my grandparents. Mom was born in the house her paternal grandparents lived in. No electricity, no gas, no water. They had a water well, a fireplace and a wood-burning cook stove. Coal oil lamps provided light. She spoke frequently of their bathroom facilities being an outhouse.

Mom was raised on a farm and developed a keen liking for gardening. Her family would plant a spring garden and a fall garden. This was where most of their food came from. She continued her love of gardening all her life.

Soon after World War II commenced, my grandparents obtained employment in Dallas at what Mom called a war plant. They left their home in Emberson and moved to Dallas. Her parents were subsequently transferred to Convair at Liberator Village near White Settlement. Convair later became known as General Dynamics, later known as Lockheed.

Mom attended high school at Tech High School in Fort Worth. She was active in sports. Volleyball was her favorite. She was a gorgeous high school debutante with an abundance of friends. She was on the Homecoming Court her senior year. The girls on the court were called Duchesses in those years.

Mom and her friends spent a lot of time at Rockwood Park in Fort Worth being together, enjoying each other's company, playing guitars and singing. Inspiration Point on Lake Worth was another favorite spot for them.

<u>Dementia or Alzheimer's ?</u>

She met my dad her senior year of high school. They were married July 1, 1950, several years after her graduation from high school. Mom's first major employment was at Southwestern Bell Telephone Company as a long-distance operator. They continued to live in White Settlement.

Mom and Dad had five children. I have an older sister and older brother, a younger brother who was stillborn and a younger sister who lived three and a half hours. Mom had twice experienced the unimaginable, the worst pain a parent can endure, the loss of a child.

She was the church secretary in the Baptist church we were members of during our entire youth. She was the secretary to the pastor who graciously eulogized her at her funeral in 2009. Mom was involved with the youth group, always keeping us involved with church activities.

She was an excellent seamstress and made most of our clothes as we were growing up. She made quilts, curtains, bedspreads, wedding dresses. What a talent! And what a cook! Every night Mom would cook full-course meals for us. She and my dad doted on their children and made sure we had a happy childhood.

Mom loved deer hunting and would go every year simply to be outdoors. She loved to be at the deer lease and enjoyed this until several years before her death.

She also had a passion for water skiing. Some of my earliest memories are of my family spending every weekend at the lake, camping, water skiing, playing volleyball.

If you ever needed a piece of furniture refinished, Mom was the go-to person. She enjoyed this gift she had. She would drive around in her SUV loading pieces of furniture people had put out for the trash and refinish the furniture to pure beauty. What a talent she had for bringing an ugly piece of furniture to something anyone would want and be proud to have in their home.

All her life, Mom was a teeny lady, only five feet tall, weighing around a hundred pounds. One of her favorite comments was *"Dynamite comes in small packages."* She was such a feisty little lady.

She had beautiful green eyes which turned more of a blue as she aged. Her hair was a gorgeous auburn color. And oh, what a funny lady she could be. Had a wonderful personality and sense of humor, especially in her younger years.

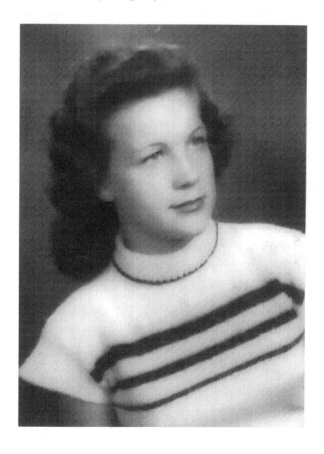

Dementia or Alzheimer's ?

Mom adored her parents. She was attentive to their needs. When I was growing up, we spent every holiday with them and spent a great amount of time at their house throughout the year. Members of our family oftentimes got together to play dominos or cards at my grandparents' home. Forty-Two was one of our favorite games.

What special grandparents we had. It was truly important to my mother for her children to know and love their grandparents. It was important to her to aid in the bond my grandparents had with us as their grandchildren.

After my grandmother's death in 1985, Mom and her siblings took care of their father for the next 15 years, even as Mom was in the throes of developing early onset dementia.

Mom and her father spent enjoyable time gardening together, either at his house or her house. Their vegetables came from their gardens. She loved flowers too. Wasn't too successful at growing them, so she would put silk flowers in her outside pots. She wanted things to look pretty in her yard, and they did.

After my parents divorced, Mom lived the last 30 years of her life in the same, quaint house, a small house on an acre lot. She frequently spoke of how grateful she was to have such wonderful neighbors. Mom's neighbors helped us keep a closer watch on her when her memory started to deteriorate in 1998 at the age of 67.

2 CHRISTMAS DAY 1999, OUR FAMILY'S REALIZATION

Holidays have always been special to me. Vivid recollections and fond memories of past Christmases, even as a small child, are distinct in my memory. Growing up, I remember our family enjoyed holidays every year at my maternal grandparents' home, where most of our extended family would gather together. Aunts, uncles, cousins. Not always everyone, but a lot of family around. And endless wonderful times.

The family gathering this holiday was at our house. We were fortunate enough to have both of my siblings and my mother there, along with nieces and nephews.

"Later on, we need to go in the other room and have a talk about Mom."

My siblings concurred.

I had known for a while something was not right with Mom. My siblings were in agreement, we needed to commence the heart-wrenching process of learning to help Mom through what we imagined to be the beginning of dementia. What had started off the year before as basic forgetfulness was now progressing to Mom telling us something, only to repeat the exact same sentence within minutes.

Being the fiercely independent and private person she was, she had gone to the doctor several years previously due to memory problems, unbeknownst to any of her family. We would later discover she had been put on the medication Aricept for her memory issues.

My active, vibrant, full-of-life Mom was slowly being consumed by this unrelenting disease. She would have received solace and support from those of us who love her. But she chose to keep it to herself for several years.

That Christmas Day in December 1999, we agreed to keep a closer eye on her, praying we were wrong. I recall one of us saying we believed she maybe had five years left. Mom was 68 years old in December 1999. She lived a little over nine more years. She continued to live alone, continued to assert her independence, preferring it this way as she had lived alone for nearly 35 years by this time.

My grandparents were married 55 years. After my grandmother died in 1985, my grandfather lived alone until his death in January 2001, two months short of his 98th birthday.

For years, at least five times a week Mom would drive 30 minutes one way to care for her father, taking meals to him she had prepared, driving him to doctor appointments, making sure his needs were tended to. In hindsight, I recognize I was not there for my mother the way I should have been. Though I was oblivious of this at the time, I am aware now of the tremendous stress caregiving put on her.

After a number of years of taking care of her father, Mom's trips to his house became less and less. She could not do it anymore. So tired, so weary.

Much of the literature regarding dementia and Alzheimer's lists stress as a large contributing factor to the disease. Mom herself was ill, though we did not know at the time.

Over the next several years, her memory deteriorated in a more rapid fashion. Other issues started to manifest themselves other than a slight memory problem and repeating herself.

"Don't ever get old."

"But Mom, the other alternative is to die young. No one wants that."

"You make an excellent point."

We both laughed.

Dementia or Alzheimer's ?

During this time, we noticed Mom would get blank stares on her face. It was as though she was fixated on something, as though her brain needed to catch up. She tried to conceal this from those around her, but it was much more obvious than she recognized. I would later learn this fixation is part of the disease process.

After Mom passed away, one of her younger sisters told me she did not like to go see Mom because she knew she could not help her when Mom would get those blank stares on her face. Others responded there were times when they believed she did not recognize them but was pretending she did.

In my conversations with Mom, there were times when I could see she had lost her train of thought. I would attempt to fill in the blanks, to help her keep talking and not experience a lost feeling. This is important in people who recognize this is happening to them. Speak for them when they cannot find the words. Mom felt at ease when I helped her get her thinking back on track, even for that moment.

We would see Post-it notes all over Mom's house, particularly in her bedroom. For years, she had made lengthy lists and written notes to remind herself what she needed to do on a particular day.

This was not uncommon. Her Post-its were now one-word descriptions. Another clue to us that something was amiss.

She was still paying her own bills. We noticed a change in her handwriting. What was beautiful handwriting was now becoming shaky handwriting, difficult to read. She would forget to put in the amount or forget to sign the check.

For several years, we noticed Mom becoming more and more irritable and reclusive. She was beginning to isolate herself, which did not allow us to observe her behavior as easily. So we made a nuisance of ourselves, trying to keep an eye on her comings and goings.

Pulling herself together for our visits was still fairly effortless for her. Yet we would see signs at her house of what was coming. In hindsight, we know now some of her explanations were feeble attempts to satisfy our questions and concerns. Mom began to discuss with me the changes occurring in her memory and overall thinking ability.

On one of the doctor visits I went to with Mom, she was given a memory test. After passing it, she became angry because she thought the test seemed dumb. She quoted the months of the year backwards, perfect. She counted backwards from 100 every seventh number, perfect.

Like many elderly, Mom had become adept at convincing the doctor there was nothing out of the ordinary with her. I believe she did this out of fear. She realized the memory problems she had been experiencing but refused to let anyone else acknowledge her issue. It may be prudent to speak with the doctor ahead of time to alert them to the hidden behaviors of your spouse or parent at home that the doctor may not be seeing in an office setting.

After Mom passed that memory test, I tried to convince myself they are wrong. Mom is not sick, she is only getting older.

"This cannot be happening to my mom, not my mom," I thought. I was with her at some of her doctor appointments. Still, this was difficult to accept.

She knew herself something was wrong but chose to deal with it on her own terms. Mom's letter to Alzheimer's is included at the end of this book, in her own handwriting.

In August 2002, I gave my beloved Mother a beautiful card expressing to her how much she meant to me. She kept the card. Now I have it. Mom had always had a fear of being put in a nursing home. I promised in the card if it was within my power to take care of her, I would, she would never go to a nursing home. I made a promise I did not know if I could keep.

But I did do everything I knew to do to take care of her, to make certain she would not be alone in her journey with this loathsome disease. I have often speculated what Mom would say if she knew how desperate we were to help her and make her life as normal as possible. I imagine she would be proud we did the same for her as she did for her parents.

Mom was not demanding at all, but she had developed a desperate, scared air about her. Her current circumstances had made her more vulnerable, something she had rarely experienced in the past. She sensed she was losing control. Mom was slowly becoming less lucid, less oriented. Denial was not an option now.

She would call me to ask questions about her finances or something she could not understand or a phone call she would get from somebody trying to sell her something. I explained to her those types of companies take advantage of elderly people and she should not answer calls she did not recognize on her caller ID or replace the receiver if she got any more calls she did not recognize. She could not fathom why people would take advantage of the elderly.

Mom bought an insurance policy from one of the callers for her vehicle which was already insured. I was able to call the company on behalf of her, speak to them in as nice a way as possible and get her money refunded. After that incident, my conversations with Mom usually included queries of whether she had had any of those annoying calls (as she called them).

From that moment on, whenever she saw a number on her caller ID she assumed was a sales call, she would pick up the receiver and disconnect the call. Before long, she started not recognizing phone numbers she had known for most of her adult life, her family's phone numbers.

That day in 1999 when my siblings and I talked, we knew our journey was beginning with Mom and this tortuous disease. A slow, painful journey. She slowly deteriorated over the next few years in truly subtle ways. We agonizingly watched her, frequently speaking with one another regarding her behaviors.

Unbeknownst to us, throughout the years Mom had been documenting a lot of her feelings, a lot of her despair. She kept a monthly calendar and wrote on it what she needed to do each day. As time progressed, she stopped documenting her errands and started documenting her feelings. The last several years of her life, she would write one or two words daily on her calendars about how she was feeling. Blah was one of her favorite words.

These calendars and some of Mom's writings show the weight of the burden she was carrying and how gracefully she was trying to cope with her illness. She did not want us involved, did not want us burdened with her. I imagine by the time my mother passed away, she knew she was not a burden to anyone. She knew she was cared for, she knew she was loved.

All those years ago, Mom was merely repeating herself. This was a sporadic occurrence, something we all do at times. As time passed, we noticed personality changes in her. She became more hostile, more withdrawn, more reclusive. We know now what all those behaviors represented, our mother was in the early stages of Alzheimer's. Mom continued to live alone as we monitored her actions and behavior.

On one of her regular trips to the bank, she walked to the police department across the street and made a police report stating her car had been stolen. We considered it had been stolen because as of this date, nothing of this magnitude had occurred. A week later, her car was found in the same parking lot of the establishment where she left it. She was adamant she had not left her car there.

We would find out some time later she was seen driving on the wrong side of a four-lane street with two lanes each direction.

"Mom, those ladies said they saw you driving on the wrong side of the street."

"They do not know what they're talking about. That was not me!"

Another time, she was lost. She got in the car with people she had never met. Thankfully, a gentleman and his wife made sure she got home safely.

It was during this time period we knew the end of Mom's independence was imminent. But we knew it would be a battle to help her. And who could blame her? Her refuge of safety and comfort, her familiar setting was becoming not so familiar.

Also during this time period, we were painfully aware Mom needed to make the transition to no driving. How do you tell your independent, stubborn mother you need her keys? In people with dementia or Alzheimer's, the car is one of the last symbols of their independence. We considered disabling Mom's car to where it would not start.

But we knew she would find a way to a car dealership and buy another one.

What do you do when someone with a malfunctioning brain is belligerent about you not knowing what you are talking about? Dear Lord, please help us come to a solution.

I contacted the police department, explained our circumstances. Hoped they would take Mom's keys and force her not to drive. I told them the scenarios of her losing her car, getting in the car with strangers, filing a police report when she imagined her car was stolen and driving on the wrong side of a four-lane, busy street. The police told me there was nothing they could do unless there was an accident or unless someone was hurt.

My siblings and I knew we should've brainstormed on how to take the keys long before the danger of driving was so apparent.

I decided to go to Mom's house to observe firsthand how she was driving. She had told me earlier on the phone she was headed to the store shortly, so I headed over there to go to the store with her. As I was driving on her street, she was pulling out of her driveway. I followed her. She drove diligently, straight to the store and back home. The store she frequented was 10 minutes from her house. I later spoke with the people in the store.

"Your mom needs help. Someone needs to be taking care of her. She seems lost, someone needs to intervene."

Mom enjoyed eating at a nearby barbecue restaurant. I had gone there with her numerous times. I spoke with the people there as well.

"She doesn't come in here much anymore, but she's not well. Somebody needs to help her."

Dear Lord, please help us understand how to help our mother.

Throughout these years, Mom had not yet been diagnosed with Alzheimer's, but she took Aricept every day and knew her memory was lacking. Though Mom's memory had been worsening for a number of years, it was not until approximately 2007 when this little 90 pound lady was given the diagnosis of Alzheimer's.

From this time on, she deteriorated rapidly. We were certain she was not taking her Aricept and not eating. For weeks and weeks, my sister and I traded out days, going every day to check on our beloved mother, taking meals to her. Mom knew if we called and she did not answer, we would come over there immediately. By this time, she had lost 15 pounds.

Christmas Day 1999, Our Family's Realization

My sister and I drove together to Mom's house to talk to her about her situation. She screamed at us, threw her medication across the room and told us we were not her daughters. What a blow to us. What were we going to do now? This happened daily for several weeks. We knew this was the disease talking, not our mother. This behavior was completely out of character for her. She was becoming another person, right before our eyes. Where was the sweet lady we knew as our mother? She was still there. This was still her.

Due to what we imagined to be dehydration and inability to care for herself and her refusal to let us help her, an ambulance was called for her. There was no other choice. Mom was past the time to be living alone. Though the stint in the hospital was only a couple days, she was never the same after that experience.

We would later learn Alzheimer's victims should not be traumatized. The chances of recovery are minimal. They need to maintain the status quo. We were not aware of this at the time. Though sometimes it is not always feasible, stability is what they need, everything remaining the same.

Several days after Mom was released from the hospital, my siblings and I spent some time at her house to figure out what to do. She stayed in her bedroom while we were outside talking. I suspected she knew what we were discussing. We talked about nursing homes, also other options. We left, extremely frustrated, still not knowing what to do.

As we expected, Mom would not hear of leaving her house. Leaving her home was not an option. There was no way she would allow anyone to live with her. This was not an option. We supposed we would have to physically take her out of there.

By early spring of 2008, she had become a total recluse. We watched her for a short time longer while we searched what to do. The outgoing, fun-loving, happy lady we knew as our mother was becoming a stranger to us. The anger, defiance, fear and sadness we saw did not resemble our mother.

Her eating patterns by now were non-existent. She would leave food out on the counter, opened but uneaten. We were certain she was forgetting to eat it, but she believed she had eaten. She was belligerent with me and my sister that she had eaten, she had taken her Aricept. We knew she was not taking her medication because we were counting it.

We would go to Mom's house and find full yogurt containers sitting out on her kitchen counter. She would tell us she had eaten it all. There would be six to eight cups of yogurt sitting there, open but the contents untouched.

On our daily visit to check on Mom, my husband and I could not get her to answer the front door. We walked around the back, entered through the unlocked door of her bedroom. She was lying on the bed asleep. We smelled the strong odor of natural gas. She had left her gas heater on in the living room. The pilot light had gone out.

Mom had been a smoker for 50 years. We watched as she slowly forgot how to smoke. But the fact she did smoke in the recent past and we smelled natural gas was extremely alarming. After she came to live with us, she never mentioned cigarettes again.

We could not get Mom to budge. She was not going anywhere (her words). We turned the gas off on the outside of her house at the meter, waited while the smell dissipated. Drove home distraught. Would we have to physically remove her from her own home?

We spoke with her doctor to alert her to what was going on. She had no advice for us except to continue to watch out for our mother. How do we watch out for her when she is in denial, refusing to accept help, refusing to leave her house, unable to or refusing to see what's happening?

Her doctor had no answer for us. Not having satisfaction from Mom's current doctor, my siblings and I made the decision to get a second opinion. All three of us together took her to another physician, hoping he would provide answers for us, tell us what to do. He wanted my mother to write a complete sentence.

"I want to go home."

This was the sentence my sweet mother wrote. She only wanted to go home. The doctor told us we would have to make some decidedly hard decisions, immediately. Mom had a Medical Power of Attorney. To enforce that, she must be declared mentally incompetent to care for herself.

If you are ever dissatisfied with any doctor you may take your loved one to, seek a second opinion. It is crucial you are comfortable and confident with any doctors you entrust your father, mother or spouse to. You must trust them, you must have faith in them. When you speak to the doctor in the presence of your loved one, include them in the conversation. It could be hurtful to them if you speak as though they are not there.

After the doctor's visit, a day or two later on one of my morning jogs, tears poured as I prayed God would tell me what to do.

We believed with Mom's personality type, a nursing home was not an option, especially since she did not need nursing care, per se. Doctors found nothing physically wrong with her.

Why would we relegate the physical care of our mother to others only because her mind was slowly deteriorating? We would not do this if it were a child with a dementing illness. I needed to discover ways to help my mother who was not suffering from any physical issues but was becoming more vulnerable to the limited thinking capacity this disease causes.

While jogging, I considered what could be a solution, even if temporary. We had to talk Mom into leaving her house with me, going on an outing, and while we were gone having all of her belongings in only her bedroom moved to our house and bringing her to our home instead of back to her home.

The idea occurred to me to take photos of Mom's bedroom, which she lived in ninety-nine percent of the time, of every piece of everything in her bedroom. Go to my home, place every piece of everything right where it was in her bedroom at her home and hope she would be convinced she was home, when, in fact, she was in the upstairs portion of our home.

I called my siblings and told them we were willing to do that, our mother could not go it alone anymore. We would have to get her to our house and figure out what to do afterwards.

We did that. We placed every picture where it was, every pencil where it was, placed her meds where they were, all of it. Placed the bedroom furniture in exactly the way it was at her home, even the rugs on the floor, the little odds and ends on her nightstand. Everything right where it was.

We placed all her toiletries in the exact same manner they were in her own bathroom. Shampoo, bar soap, hair spray, perfume, everything. I want to believe my mother imagined she was at home. It was heartbreaking to observe. But the pain I experienced watching my mother deteriorate right before my eyes paled in comparison to the pain, the anguish, the hopelessness I could only imagine she felt.

She had been at our house about two weeks when I recognized my husband and I could not do it on our own. We both worked full-time jobs. So we hired caregivers to come in several hours a day, none of which worked out due to Mom's extreme anger.

We spent every evening with her, talking to her, playing board games with her. She did not know what she was doing with the games, but we were with her, she loved our presence and that's what mattered.

When we were not upstairs with Mom, she would walk around repeatedly calling my name. She was so lost. My heart broke for her. The only help we could be was to make her as comfortable as possible in our home, to be her security every chance we could, be her safe place to fall when she became distraught and frightened, when she cried because she could not remember.

One of the greatest tolls on me was emotionally, watching my mother's mind deteriorate rapidly over the last six months of her life. I could not bring her to our reality, we had to enter her reality.

I contemplated hard to find the right words to say to her when she would get so frustrated because she could not remember something.

"Now Mom, it's on a need-to-remember basis, and you don't need to remember."

Mom always loved it when I spoke those words to her.

"Mom, it's on a need-to-know basis, and you don't need to know."

"Oh, hon, thank you so much for telling me that. That makes me feel so much better."

If I helped her see how unimportant it was to remember something, she seemed not to dwell on it as much.

Consider anything to say or do to put their mind at ease, bring them some type of comfort. They may not be able to express their thoughts, but they have feelings. Reassure them daily how much you love them, remind them you and your family are there for them, walking this journey with them.

Three months after Mom came to live with us, I came close to a full-blown nervous breakdown. I knew I could no longer handle the enormous responsibility of caregiving myself. My husband and I came to the painful realization we would have to try assisted living for my mother.

I took her to the facility we had chosen, stayed with her in her "room" for as long as I could, left there sobbing. This particular facility had the notion the family should have no contact for the first seven days. I knew I would never be able to stay away, so my husband and I left on a trip. That was the longest week of my life.

The day we got back, I made a beeline to the facility, knowing I would leave there heartbroken. My mom looked content and seemed happy to see me. She was comforting me as I wept.

They told me she had been doing okay, staying to herself, not eating much but content. Over the next three months, my husband and I visited Mom on a daily basis. It was always difficult to leave. She would tell me to come back to see her when I could. Though I would go see her daily, she would react as though it had been forever since she had seen me. Victims of this disease have little, if any, perception of time.

At this particular facility, the residents had a small room as their bedroom, the room they lived in. It was a huge building with a large common area they wanted all the residents to congregate in. The idea is to coerce everyone to be sociable, get to know the other residents.

There was a beautiful, huge backyard.

"Is this whole thing my house?"

This was Mom's question while we were sitting outside in the swing.

"Yes, Mom, I guess it is your house."

"Well, how come it feels so small inside?"

She spent most of her time in her small room. Broke my heart.

31

Mom had spent the last 10 years of her life being a loner, which we knew could be a problem for her in a facility. We sensed she likely would not communicate or attempt to make friends. We were right. She stayed to herself and was often hateful and hurtful to the other residents. This was a place where the elderly were forgetting everything about their life in much the same way she was forgetting hers.

I did not want to make another change for Mom, another disruption for her, but I knew she was miserable there. She was becoming even more depressed and introverted. After three months, my husband and I decided to try, once again, at our house, this time with a full-time, live-in caregiver. I was determined to help my mother. She cared for and nurtured me my whole life. It was my turn.

At this time, we moved all of Mom's household furniture from her house to the upstairs part of our house. We tried to surround her with her own belongings of her entire house, not only her bedroom. We tried to make the upstairs part of our house look as much like Mom's house as possible.

Our live-in caregiver was Mary. We found her through a caregiving service. She was so patient with Mom. So thoughtful and affectionate, even when Mom was hateful. We believe Mom grew to love her. Mary is the last word I heard my mother say.

We put Mom's belongings all around her living area, trying to keep the colors subdued and simple as this is less busy, less confusing and frightening. We hung pictures of movie stars. Marilyn Monroe, Diana Ross and Elvis Presley. Mom loved looking at those pictures. Depending on the advancement of the disease, it is sometimes beneficial to put mementos from their early years in their living area. This may be more familiar for them.

We kept calming tunes playing as much as we could. She loved gospel melodies, so that's what was usually playing low on the stereo in her living area. Music is a wonderful way to improve their mood (and yours), a way of calming anxiety and agitation. Music provides a way to connect and interact. Mom would sometimes talk about the singers as though she knew them. She did take to the music well. She and I would sit and listen together, no talking, simply listening to the calming songs. It brought Mom pleasure and a feeling of relief, something familiar. Even caught her tapping her toe at times.

Mom had a favorite chair she sat in for years. She continued to sit in it at our house. I had noticed she had some bruising on her frail arms when she first came to live with us. We put padding on the arms of her favorite chair. The bruising faded. The padding made her so much more comfortable. This was a problem she could not find the basic solution to due to her disease.

Often, folks with this disease are unable to be inventive enough to find solutions to issues. Be flexible. Use your imagination. If there is a problem such as the arms on Mom's chair, consider ways to combat the problem. With each problem that arises, there is likely a solution.

We also put cushions on the edge of the tub so if she hit herself she would not bruise or get hurt in some other way. Grab bars were installed around the toilet and around the tub. We had rugs on the floor in the bath because Mom's feet were always cold, even when she had socks or house shoes on. We taped the rugs to the floor all the way around the border of the rugs. It is crucial to tape all rugs to the floor and tape any kind of step-ups such as from a tiled floor to a carpeted floor. The difference in the floor textures could confuse your loved one. The tape may make the transition smoother.

Mom loved to sit on the edge of her bed. She would rest her feet on the frame rail. After she lost so much weight, it would be painful for her to put her feet on the rail, so she would not sit on her bed anymore. I put padding on the frame rail, the part where her feet would go, and she started to sit there again. She would sit on the bed, I would sit in her chair and we would chat. When there is an issue such as the rail, you can often find a solution.

It is crucial to help your loved one sense they are loved and valued. Talk even when there's nothing to talk about. Talk about anything. The curtains, the bedspread, birds outside the window chirping. Sometimes Mom and I would talk about the distant past. She had little trouble remembering where she grew up, where she attended church. Yet she did not remember the house she lived in for 30 years. As her illness progressed, she would question if she was my mother. Such a wicked disease.

Mom frequently walked around our house saying *"I want to go home."* While she lived here, we often took rides to get out of the house for a while. I decided one day to take her to her house to see if she remembered it and truly wanted to go there. Mary, our caregiver, had agreed if Mom wanted to be home to live out her final days, she would live with her at her own home. As we pulled into the driveway, I sensed the lost feeling in Mom. We proceeded inside. She did not remember anything about the house she had spent 30 years in. Such a dehumanizing disease.

Did Mom want to go "home" to Heaven? Maybe that was the home she wanted to go to when she repeatedly expressed she wants to go home. She spoke frequently of seeing her mom soon in Heaven. We had a large picture of my grandmother hanging in Mom's bedroom at our home. She would constantly look at the picture and comment about her mom and seeing her again. I am confident she never forgot who her mother was.

I like to believe she never forgot who we were. Even till the end, I had some meaningful talks with Mom, maybe not so much talking as simply sitting, holding hands. I would roll her hair on sponge rollers sometimes and style it for her. I'd put a smidge of lipstick or lip gloss on her. Sometimes I'd give her a manicure and pedicure, polish her nails. At times, I would rub her feet. She loved the attention, and I could tell it made her sense she was pretty. If you cannot help with your loved one's hair, have a stylist come to your home, if feasible. If your loved one's hair is kept clean and looking pretty, they will likely be in a better mood. Compliment them frequently. Mom loved it when I would tell her how beautiful her hair was or how great her nails looked.

Christmas Day 1999, Our Family's Realization

We were aware Mom could not remember what day of the week it was or what month it was. This was frustrating for her. We made signs of what month and day of the week it was and hung it daily. Mom was so happy because she did not have to worry about remembering it anymore.

By this time, I was not certain Mom knew who I was. I like to hope she did, but I have no way of knowing. I would constantly tell her who I was and who she was. Some days she would put her hands on my face, bring it close to hers and ask me if I was her daughter.

"Hon, are you my daughter?"

"Yes, Mom, I'm your baby girl."

"Well no wonder I love you so much," she would say with a grin on her face.

"Am I your mother?"

"Yes, Mom, I'm your baby girl."

"Well no wonder I love you so much."

I was unsure at this time how much of her previous world she could remember, how much of my previous world she could remember. I knew I wanted to be in her current world, whatever she found it to be. I missed her the way she used to be. With dementia, though, you do not live the way it used to be, you live the way it is now. Mom may not have known who I was, but I knew who she was.

We were also painfully aware Mom was forgetting who our relatives were, so we got a huge frame with cutouts in the mat, put a picture of all the immediate family in the cutouts and wrote their name above each one. With the names printed above the picture, she could recognize faces. But as time passed, she could no longer even do that. Mom stopped looking at the picture.

3   YOUR SUSPICION, YOUR REALIZATION

While researching what was happening to Mom, we discovered videos and an abundance of literature available on-line regarding how Alzheimer's affects the brain. Memory loss is not always the first sign of Alzheimer's or the other types of dementias.

Swift, extreme personality changes sometimes occur which could signal the onset of the disease. Is a loved one who used to be brave, trusting and responsible becoming more fearful or suspicious or confused? Are they losing interest in activities they used to enjoy? This was quite evident in our mom.

Often, loved ones will notice their family member doing activities which may not make sense to others. Perhaps they are telling the same story over and over or asking the same questions repeatedly. Or they may get fixated on a story or object to the point that it is always uppermost in their mind.

We observed all these signs in Mom. Her personality drastically changed. She tried valiantly to maintain her independence. Yet she knew and we knew her independence was coming to an end.

"Wait till you get my age, you'll forget too."
"I know, Mom. I know I will."

We have heard it our whole life. In midlife, we expect to experience forgetfulness. Forget where you put your keys? We all do it, at any age. There may be a problem if you find the keys in the refrigerator or forget what the keys are for. Can't recall the name of someone you recently met? We all do it, at any age. If you can't remember recently meeting them, there may be a problem. If your loved one calls objects by the wrong name or stops in the middle of conversations, if they repeat themselves momentarily, if they ask for the same information over and over, it may be time to consider dementia.

We noticed Mom losing her train of thought frequently. In the same conversation, she would repeatedly ask what we were talking about. In the beginning of Mom's illness, this did not concern us. As time passed, it became more and more difficult to have a conversation with her.

We are all, at times, unable to recall the word we are looking for. Those with dementia will use the wrong word entirely. The frequency of this occurrence is relevant as well. In everyday life, we may forget parts of certain situations or experiences. The person who forgets the whole situation or the whole experience may have early onset dementia.

Other signs could include neglecting responsibilities that had previously been important. You may notice them having a more difficult time doing routine chores or making important decisions that ordinarily would have been an easy decision. Or they may have problems performing familiar, everyday obligations of life. Maybe they are letting their bills go unpaid or having trouble managing their finances. We may have trouble occasionally balancing a checkbook, but the person with dementia may forget what numbers are or take much longer to balance their checkbook due to confusion. Also losing money, a noticeable deterioration in personal hygiene, a change in sleeping habits, sleeping more or sleeping less, a noticeable increase or decrease in weight.

Mom's sleeping habits became entirely erratic. She preferred her bedroom to be extremely hot. I believe the extreme heat interfered with her sleep. Her eating was also erratic. We would go out to dinner. She would not eat. She would move the food around on her plate. Though it was over a long period of time, we noticed her loss of weight.

They may forget how to dress appropriately. They may put on a sweater or turn on a heater when it is 90 degrees outside. They may turn on the air-conditioning when it is 30 degrees outside. We had this issue with Mom. She would turn on four or five space heaters in her bedroom. We would break out in a sweat, but she would say she was cold.

If someone withdraws who has been fairly social and outgoing for most of their life, if they become less willing to interact with others, they may be aware of other's suspicions of dementia in them and be embarrassed or even depressed about it. They may even suspect it in themselves and cope with these feelings by withdrawing. Or they may not even recognize they are withdrawing. Mom's neighbors told us they noticed her withdrawing, keeping to herself. This was not like Mom at all. She had so much pleasure visiting with her neighbors.

You may notice they are putting items in strange places. Their yard may not be as manicured as it once was. Their house may be much more cluttered and not as clean. They may forget routes they have been traveling for years.

These are a handful of the behaviors which might be readily visible. Keep in mind, the person with a confused brain may be accomplished at concealing their inability to remember, especially in the early phase of this disease.

We noticed this in Mom. She tried hard to conceal what was happening to her. She refused to give in to this illness stealing all of her treasured memories. She would attribute it to getting older or being too tired.

Be alert to their behavior. Even a slight sickness such as a cold can exacerbate their inability to function normally. If you have noticed a slow decline, something causing stress may rapidly worsen their condition. Discuss your observations with them before something disastrous occurs.

At one point or another, we all may engage in the above-mentioned red flags. When a number of these become apparent and frequent, we should be concerned about the possibility of early onset dementia.

Also, keep in mind numerous symptoms of Alzheimer's disease are also symptoms of other diseases such as stroke, heart disease or thyroid imbalance. Alzheimer's is only one form of dementia. Lewy body dementia, Parkinson's disease with dementia, vascular dementia and frontotemporal dementia are others. Through my research, I learned Alzheimer's is the most common form of dementia. Your loved one's physician is the only person who can correctly diagnose.

Whatever form of dementia your loved one has, they will need your compassionate care and unconditional love to help them through the ravages of this illness.

Remember, there is no set pattern for changes caused by dementia. It is different for every individual. Every person will not experience every symptom. This disease usually begins markedly slow, becoming more extreme as time passes. Some people's behavior will fluctuate weekly, some daily, some hourly.

Bear in mind your loved one's behavior is likely beyond their control. What you are observing in them is the result of damage to their brain, not because of an unpleasant personality. You will most likely not be able to reason out their behavior. It might be frustrating for you. But remember, you cannot change their behavior.

Their cognitive function will continue to deteriorate, but their quality of life can be maintained with the help of you and their family. Common sense and resourcefulness will make everyone's life less stressful.

Watch your loved one's symptoms and progression. Document everything in order to help the caregiver care for them when the time comes. Encourage other family members to document what they observe.

When we first had a suspicion of Mom's memory issues 10 years before her death, we neglected to document what we observed. In hindsight, I recognize how the simple act of documenting would have been the prudent action to take. When Mom needed a higher level of care, from the passage of time we could not remember the answers to numerous questions we were asked from those in the medical field.

If you suspect dementia in yourself or in a loved one, initiate making plans now for how this will be handled in the future. If you do this now, you can plan this for yourself instead of relying on other family members to do this painful but necessary task.

Before I knew anything at all about this disease, Mom would tell me something, only to repeat the exact same words within a minute or two.

"You told me that a second ago."

Not knowing what was to come, I would say those hurtful words to my mom.

Dementia or Alzheimer's ?

"Mom, don't you remember telling me that a moment ago?"

If I had known at the time what I know now, I would have never said those things. I did not know anything at all about the road my mom was about to embark on.

4 ACCEPTANCE AND PLANNING

"Family is where we first experience love and where we first give it. It's probably the first place we've been hurt by someone we love, and hopefully the place we learn love can overcome even the most painful rejection. We don't have to use the words of theology to talk about God. People who are close to death almost never do. We should learn from those who are dying that the best way to teach our children about God is by loving each other wholly and forgiving each other fully." Kerry Egan, Hospice Chaplain in Massachusetts

The early stage of this disease can linger on for some time. Alzheimer's is a progressive brain disease caused by sticky plaques forming in the brain, sometimes referred to as tangles. As of today, there is no cure for this relentless destruction of the brain.

If your family member has been diagnosed with dementia or Alzheimer's, you are aware of their destiny. It is imperative for you not to live in fear of this disease. Living in fear of the disease will only hurt you, your loved one and all those around you.

I learned this the hard way. My anxiety and fear of helping my mother as she progressed through this disease sometimes overpowered me. I would have to reason things through, regroup and come back to acceptance, compassion and faith. There were times when my angst did not allow me to handle the situation with the grace and dignity I had hoped to maintain throughout Mom's illness. Never took my angst out on my mother, but I thanked God countless times for my understanding, loving husband.

Throughout our journey with Mom, I grew to appreciate the realization and acceptance that dementia does not have to be a death sentence for the caregiver. You learn to live a new normal. And the new normal may change every day. You can and will change with it. Celebrate what is, not what was.

As much as you can, be a voice for your loved one. Learn as much as possible about their illness. The 36 Hour Day, authored by Nancy L. Mace, M.A. and Peter V. Rabins, M.D., is an excellent book to gain insight. I read this book and referred back to this book frequently. Explore your options. Know what questions to ask.

Oftentimes, people will say oh, she might live another year, she might live six more months. We imagined Mom would live maybe five more years. She lived nine more years. You must not assume your loved one's time left on this earth. With this disease, one year could turn into 10, even 20.

Document all you will be doing for your loved one in the weeks and months to come as you embark on caregiving. You never know when the knowledge you glean from your experience will help someone else in your same situation.

You may experience an urgent need to fix your loved one's illness, to normalize their behavior. You may convince yourself they will get better, that this is not happening. Denial is part of the grief process. I sometimes found myself in denial. Refused to accept I would lose my mother.

Work diligently to come to terms with what is happening to your loved one. Work every day to gain a deeper understanding about this disease. You will not be able to keep them in your world, you must enter their new world. Accept that you cannot fix this. See them as they are, not how you want them to be or wish them to be or believe they should be.

What you can do is help them experience some semblance of happiness every day and live out their remaining days free from pain, if possible, and at peace. This was one of my goals with Mom, to help her have some sort of happiness and peace every day. Even something as simple as telling her she looked pretty put a smile on her face.

For some people, it is difficult to accept your family member has a disease that will not get better, that there is no cure for. Even if you need to seek counseling to help you through this time, it is imperative you accept reality for what it is. Though you will recognize your loved one, they could become a stranger to you. Accept the present moment and remember eventually this time will pass. At this time, however, they need you to help them cope with this devastating disease.

If you suspect dementia onset in your loved one, it is important they have an advanced directive and a Power of Attorney in place. We were fortunate Mom had all her legal papers in order. My knowledge is very limited on this subject. I encourage you to seek the advice of an attorney in these matters. Taking responsibility for someone else's decisions is a complex task. Seek legal counsel to be sure of your responsibilities in these matters.

The healthcare Power of Attorney allows a trusted individual to make health care decisions on behalf of another person who may not be able to make their own health care decisions. The financial Power of Attorney allows a trusted individual to make financial decisions on behalf of another person who may not be able to make their own financial decisions. This would include paying bills or paying expenses by liquidating assets.

The ideal situation would be to have these documents completed and notarized before any suspicion of dementia or any other disease occurs. However, oftentimes we neglect these important measures until it becomes necessary to have them and they are not there.

As a court reporter, I have been the reporter for countless proceedings where the family is at odds with one another, embroiled in legal battles due to parents with no legal documents in place.

As soon as possible, obtain clear, written wishes of your loved one. Help them fill out a living will along with an advanced directive. An advanced directive goes into effect only when someone has a terminal or irreversible disease. The documents can typically be obtained on-line.

These legal documents need to be in place to tell medical personnel as well as family members what someone's wishes are in the event they are unable to participate in discussions of these matters. If it is feasible to do so, consult with other family members regarding this. Get their input, especially if your family has been able to problem solve in the past.

Does your father, mother or spouse want to be on life-sustaining measures? With no directive in place, family members will likely disagree on this. Ask your loved one if you can go to their doctor's appointments with them. Ask them to give their doctor permission to speak with another family member.

A HIPAA (Health Insurance Portability and Accountability Act) release is a form which allows designated persons access to your medical records. We all need a filled-out, signed HIPAA form. This form can be obtained on-line. It is my understanding most doctors' offices or law offices have these forms on hand.

These documents may already be signed and in place. Does any family member know where they are kept? Does the doctor have them? Maybe a minister or clergy? Someone, preferably the Power of Attorney, needs to know where all these forms are kept. If they are in a lockbox or safe, a family member or trusted person should be made aware of where the key is or what the combination is.

If one dies without a will, the estate will be divided in probate court and a Judge will decide who gets what. This can deplete the estate monetarily and take months if not years in court. Verbal statements of your loved one's wishes will likely not be given credence in court.

If there are no legal documents in place, the estate could end up in probate before a Judge who will likely rule solely on what the law is, not on what someone's unwritten wishes are. With no legal documents in place, doctors may not be able to discuss medical information with family. Your loved one might not have their wishes fulfilled. The decisions involving bank accounts and property could be left to total strangers.

If they have bank accounts or investment accounts, is there more than one authorized user on the accounts? Maybe they would be willing to have a joint account with you so you could oversee their affairs. If you are on their account, keep a logbook of every penny you spend on their behalf. Keep detailed, meticulous records. If your decisions or motives are ever questioned, you will have a logbook to refer to.

Not everyone is willing to discuss these legalities. But the best time to have this discussion is before there is a problem or when you notice early signs of possible health problems. Attempt to broach the subject in a way that it is obvious you are trying to help them and help your family.

Dementia or Alzheimer's ?

"Mom, I know we have talked about this in the past, but if something were to happen to you, I am not sure I could be in the right frame of mind to remember what we said. Could we talk about it again? Don't you think it would give you and our family peace of mind if we put it in writing? I'll fill mine out with you. We'll make it a joint effort."

If your loved one has a pet, you could put it in the form of a directive regarding their beloved pet.

"Mom, what would you want us to do with your precious pet?"

Being the fiercely independent woman our mother was, it was difficult for her to relinquish her personal business to her children. She took care of her finances for as long as she possibly could. She did not allow me to pay her bills for her until her handwriting became difficult to read.

It is not uncommon for the elderly to find it difficult to allow their grown children to take control of their finances or even help with the management of their finances. Regardless, it is sometimes essential in order to protect investments and assets, especially if one's ability to manage their own is diminished.

Paranoia is sometimes present in people with dementia, even early onset dementia. So they may worry their adult children are after their money or complete control of their finances. Someone, preferably their Power of Attorney, needs to know what financial institutions they have accounts at and what their account numbers are. Maybe have an accountant or a financial planner.

When you have this discussion of legal documents and finances initially with your parent, try not to question their competence. Tell them you want to help them, you know the responsibility is onerous on them. I did this with Mom. When she understood I was trying to make life simpler for her, she seemed to be relieved not to worry about it anymore.

Again, say you are doing the same for yourself with your own documents. This makes it less threatening to your parent. You might ask them for their advice relating to your own documents. This could help them perceive it as a family effort, not an attack on their mental stability.

As you embark on this journey with your loved one and their illness, you will likely lose a small part of them each day. There are five stages of grief: denial and isolation, anger, guilt or bargaining, sadness or depression, and acceptance. You will possibly experience all of these. They do not necessarily happen in that order and will likely occur more than once during your loved one's illness. They did for me.

When Mom first experienced problems with her memory, I refused to accept it. Maybe she is simply getting older. Maybe it is merely a side effect of her medication. As time passed, my refusal to accept it and the denial dissipated. I knew Mom had a problem. So I set out to do whatever I could to learn about this disease, to learn how to best help her and to keep the vow I made to her long ago to always be there for her, to not let her go to a nursing home if at all possible and to keep my love for her unconditional as she had always done for me.

Surround your loved one with gentle acceptance. Dementia and/or Alzheimer's will win in the end. Don't try to fix it. Don't pretend you have the essential answers. You will experience powerlessness. You will suspect your loved one is out of your grasp. You will not be able to stop the barrage of this mind-altering disease. What you can do is accept it and plan for it, to the best of your ability.

If you have siblings, it might be advantageous to have a family meeting. Bear in mind, everyone in your family may not want to be involved in a meeting. In fact, it is possible not everyone will want to have a part in the planning or strategies to help the family member with this illness. You do not have to agree with their decision, but you do have to accept it and not let it cause bitterness or anger in you. Those feelings will drain your energy.

Everyone does not necessarily have to be in the same room to discuss the situation at hand. There may be family members who want to participate via remote means such as FaceTime or Skype.

The meeting place should be in a comfortable location free of outside disturbances or interruptions. Everyone involved should be allowed their own opinion, their own emotions. This family meeting is no place for ridicule, criticism or anger towards one another. Let every person present share their feelings about the situation.

Make an effort to identify what each person's role and responsibility will be. It could be helpful to recap everything talked about and document it so there will be no question about who does what. The ideal outcome would be that everyone is on the same page when the meeting is over.

Keep in mind, however, not everyone will see eye to eye on everything. Every issue or problem may not be resolved at one family meeting. Other family issues and problems could arise during the course of this disease. Your family might not have perfect harmony at all times. As the caregiver, attempt to do your best to keep everyone in the loop. Have family meetings frequently to keep everyone informed of what is happening and to re-evaluate the arrangements, if necessary.

5 CAREGIVING

If you have been advised by a physician that your father or mother, husband or wife has been diagnosed with some form of dementia, as their caregiver you may frequently suffer loneliness and desperation, as I did. Oftentimes you will not know what to do or say next.

Few caregivers are prepared for the enormity of the responsibility they are undertaking when their parent or spouse is diagnosed with dementia, Alzheimer's or any other disease. My husband and I had no idea what we were embarking on when we agreed to care for Mom. But when we made the commitment, I delved deep into literature and educational Web sites on the issues at hand.

Gain as much knowledge and insight as possible from healthcare professionals regarding your loved one's condition. You will not be able to remember it all, so take notes of your conversations with them and at meetings you have with them. You will undoubtedly refer back to those notes as time goes on in your loved one's illness and their treatments and conditions change.

Your feelings will run the gamut from grief to anger, guilt to resentment. Acknowledge these feelings, accept they are part of your new daily living and let them go. Remember, it is always your choice to be angry and resentful of your caregiving role or to do and say every word with love and provide the compassionate care they need. Know what your limits are. You did nothing to cause this illness your loved one has. Keep your guilt feelings at bay. It will not be helpful for anyone if you let those feelings consume you.

Negative feelings in the face of caregiving, I have come to learn, is suffered by most caregivers. Undoubtedly, you will experience resentment, sadness, isolation, impatience, stress and frequently be overwhelmed. You will also experience gratitude, sweetness, tenderness, patience, purpose. You will remember the fond memories you have of your loved one.

I found myself feeling resentful toward my beloved mother only one time. Resentment that she was no longer the mother I knew, she was no longer the mother I grew up with. My resentment was short-lived, as it takes only a moment to remember this was through no fault of hers.

Having negative, even furious feelings about caregiving is perfectly normal. You love the person you are taking care of, but you hate the situation you are in. You cannot control the situation you have found yourself in, but you can control the way you react to it. You can smile and laugh, you can be aware of the warmth of your loved one's touch and they can be aware of yours. Alzheimer's cannot take those feelings away.

You may have trouble concentrating and find yourself in a perpetual state of worry. Physical ailments such as headaches, back and neck pain and weight loss or gain could come on suddenly. Exhaustion could be a weekly occurrence for you, if not a daily occurrence. You might develop problems with sleep.

Keep in mind, burnout and exhaustion will not help your loved one, it will only contribute to the hopelessness they feel. Aim to get daily exercise for yourself. Simple stretching exercises could be beneficial. Take naps when your loved one takes naps. Rest your mind. Take a warm bath while they are napping. Cleaning house and playing piano was therapeutic for me.

If you are the only caregiver, it is possible the health of you is even more urgent than that of your ill loved one. Your stamina and endurance will continuously be tested while you are a caregiver. But you must be well yourself to take care of another.

<u>Dementia or Alzheimer's ?</u>

I regularly reminded myself my health and attitude would have a profound effect on my mother's health and welfare. I found that as soon as I became calm, accepted Mom's destiny and joined her in this journey, life became simpler for both of us. My husband and I became bound and determined to make her road as pleasant as possible.

During the journey you are beginning, you will connect with other folks traveling the same road you are. You can find tremendous solace by participating in a support group. You may be hesitant to consider a support group. Try it anyway. You could find it is exactly what you need. Other caregivers can be extremely empowering.

I relied on friends and family as well as other caregivers to be our support. Mom's friends were also supportive. I bent lots of ears and borrowed many shoulders during this time.

You truly are not alone in the journey you are embarking on of frustration, heartbreak and endless moments of joy and peace. People often do not appreciate the complexities of caregiving unless they have done it themselves.

In your particular situation, no one may have inquired of you as to whether you want to be or can be the caregiver. Nor does anyone tell you or explain to you what it might mean. If you have chosen to be the caregiver or if you were chosen to be the caregiver, remember you are the backbone of your loved one's immediate future. You will be the one to preserve their dignity of life in those times when they are not be able to. You will be the one they rely on and look to for comfort, for security, for love.

Keep your loved one's life as normal as possible. This disease is relentless. But as time goes on, you will find yourself thinking of unique ways for you and your loved one to cope. In this book, I have shared some of our ways of coping, some of our ways of seeing issues before they even arose.

Through taking care of my own mother and through intense research, I learned one of the heartbreaking aspects of this disease is the impaired person has almost no ability to control their own emotions, often lashing out at you when what they want to do is hug you. The hateful words that come out of their mouth are not the loving words they are thinking.

Mom never got hateful with us, but we did see her get hateful with others. Everyone was understanding because they knew this was not my mom speaking, it was her disease.

Dementia or Alzheimer's ?

People with this disease have damaged brains with restricted ability to comprehend and communicate. They are often confused, frightened and anxious because they cannot make sense of what they hear or see or even feel. They may need extra time to recognize what you are saying. In the latter stages, it is likely they will have no idea what is happening at the present moment, nor what happened in the moment immediately before the present moment.

You will see dramatic, inconsistent behaviors in your father, mother or spouse who lives with dementia. You should expect it will be erratic, random and unpredictable. They may become embarrassed due to not being able to communicate a need or want. Empathy will help in this situation. The neurons in their brain are firing erratically. They cannot control this. This could cause panic in them. The caregiver must be able to adapt to unexpected changes.

Paranoia is sometimes present in the person with this unrelenting disease. It can be difficult to deal with paranoia in another person, but try to remember they are quickly losing the ability to distinguish reality from fantasy. If you tell them they are "only being paranoid," they will likely experience hurt feelings and become defensive.

Acknowledge their feelings in a calm manner and move on. If they accuse you of stealing from them, help them look for the missing item. Reassure them you will try to find it. Try changing the subject. Within minutes, they will not be thinking about what they cannot find.

Mom hid items on several occasions and could not remember where she put something. She imagined someone had moved something. I persuaded her to look for the item. Through the search, I changed the subject and she forgot about it. This is a simple idea that helped to ease Mom's frustration.

There may be times when your loved one is angry or hostile. They may have angry outbursts. If they are prone to outbursts, it is perhaps best to avoid public places such as restaurants. Often people do not know how to react to a person with memory issues who are having an outburst. They may not comprehend it is not the person but their disease causing them to behave in this way.

Try not to react to their anger, you will likely exacerbate it. And their anger will usually be short-lived. But it is a natural part of the disease of dementia. Please do not scold them. This disease is frightening for them.

Make every effort to engage them in something calming. Maybe singing or dancing. Drawing a picture might be calming for them. Sit outside and listen to the chirping birds. Go get an ice cream cone. Go to the park and watch the toddlers play. Or go people watching somewhere. Oftentimes, people enjoy observing other folks go about their errands.

Mom enjoyed when I brushed her hair. It was relaxing to her. Seemed to calm her when she was angry. Sometimes I would roll her hair on sponge rollers. She enjoyed this as well and loved how her hair looked when we styled it.

Every day, every hour, every minute you are taking care of your loved one, please continue to remember this is no fault of theirs. They do not have a choice. You are the only one with a choice. You have a choice to accept and adjust to the present circumstances.

It is imperative to not see yourself as crucial to your loved one's progress. They will have pleasant days and poor days, with or without you. You cannot presume they have terrific days because of you. Nor should you presume they have poor days because of you. They need you to provide comfort and security for them every single day, whether the day is great or lousy.

As a caregiver, I often found myself experiencing the awful sense of guilt. Am I doing enough? What am I missing? Am I being the wife I should be? While Mom was still here I learned guilt is perfectly normal. You question *"is this ever going to be over, am I ever going to get my life back again."* It is not selfish to have these feelings, it is human.

As there is no set pattern for the disease, there should be no set pattern in the care of the person. Your expectations one day may need to be adjusted for the next day because your loved one's wants and needs will change daily, sometimes hourly, sometimes moment by moment. They may love gardening one day, loathe it the next day. They may love ice cream one day, hate it the next day.

Trying to reason with them or convince them they are wrong about something will leave you both frustrated. Whatever they are thinking, whatever they rely on, let them have those feelings. You most likely will not be able to get them on the same page as you are. These efforts will usually be met with disappointment for you and your loved one. You will have to learn to adjust to erratic behaviors in your quest to help them through this disease.

Dementia or Alzheimer's ?

We never knew what kind of mood Mom was going to be in. But we knew providing her with love, comfort and security would not change.

It might not seem like it in the beginning, but as time moves on, you will devise strategies to cope with the vacillating behaviors of your loved one. My goal with my mom was to provide whatever happiness I could for her and to make certain she was safe, taken care of and loved, even through the depression, anxiety, anger and paranoia she exhibited.

It is best not to make any rash decisions. Mull over everything before you act. Consider how it will impact you, your loved one, your own personal family. Every decision you make could affect everyone. Challenges may seem insurmountable. They are not. Your strength will be taxed to its limits. This is not about you, though. This is about your loved one who can no longer care for themselves.

If the person with the incapacitating illness is still able to live in their own home, they are likely able to communicate adequately. However, your body language is extremely relevant during this difficult time. Pay close attention to it. No matter how hard I tried to disguise my body language, Mom seemed to read me accurately.

"Are you okay, hon?"

She frequently asked me that question.

"Mom, if you're okay, I'm okay."

Your facial expressions and tone of voice will have an impact. Even if someone cannot recall the words they are trying to say, they can still sense tone. If your ill family member senses you are upset with them or feels like you are impatient with them, they might think you are angry with them.

Put yourself in their shoes. How would you handle it if your brain was unraveling and you knew it? They already suspect they are a burden to you. Acting as though they are a burden will only intensify their fear. The nonverbal cues your loved one receives from you will register with them.

It is crucial not to be condescending to them. Instead, encourage them however you can. Always remember their brain is changing due to this dreadful disease. Being nervous or agitated with them will only contribute to a worsening of their fear and frustrations.

We all at times lash out in anger and frustration when we are stressed. So will your loved one. You will eventually learn which nonverbal routines work best for you. Strive to have patience through their growing inability to communicate adequately.

Again, bear in mind this is not their fault. Your loved one will recognize when they are being treated with respect and when they are not. They will recognize when they are being cared for with love. This is a universal feeling that never goes away. Love and care can be experienced perpetually.

It is important to remember whatever your role was with your loved one, whether it be parent, child, spouse or sibling, that role is still present and always will be. You will forever be the parent, the child, the spouse, the sibling. The heart of your relationship should remain the same as it was before this illness. It may seem as if roles have been reversed. They have not. You may be caring for your parent, but regardless of their physical or mental health, they will forevermore be your parent.

It is demeaning to speak to your loved one as though they are a child. They could sense this and withdraw. Preserve the dignity they have left by speaking to them adult to adult. Your form of communication has a great impact on your loved one. If you are stressed out, exhausted, frustrated, as we get sometimes when dealing with our toddlers, your loved one could be conscious of this and have a negative reaction.

As importantly, speaking to others in the presence of your confused family member as though they are not in the room only agitates them. This is demeaning to anyone. If you need to discuss them with another person, it may be discreet to go to another room. As much as possible, include them in conversations. Help them join in.

Perhaps there is something they would like to do or something they miss doing. There may be someone they had a close friendship with. They would undoubtedly love to visit their friend. While Mom lived with us, she would get phone calls from a couple of her friends. It always meant so much to her. I could not be entirely certain she understood who they were, but it was always a pleasant experience for her to talk to someone. This disease has a tendency to cause loneliness in its victims and the caregivers.

Aim to make some fun out of everything. Take a drive to the country or maybe visit their hometown. Some elderly people enjoy trips to the zoo to observe animals, especially baby animals. Maybe there is a place your loved one enjoyed in past times. Take them for a visit to that place.

Pets often help make the world of dementia less lonely. Dogs and cats provide affection and sometimes help to alleviate stress and boredom. They provide companionship. Having a pet can also help someone concentrate on something besides their physical issues and preoccupation with aging. They have lots of time to spend with a pet, a plus for what could otherwise be an unwanted animal. Your loved one will have someone to talk to, bond with, share everyday life with, have fun with. Pets can be trained to assist your loved one in ways you may not consider, even alerting others of an emergency. There is more information on this topic on-line.

When an elderly person is at times disoriented or confused, reacts more slowly to situations, requires constant reminders or can no longer hear adequately, it could be time to take the keys. You may notice subtle evidence such as slight dents in the car they cannot explain. Ride along in the car with them to observe their driving.

Before approaching your parent about their driving, do research on other forms of transportation. Have a plan in mind to present to them regarding how they could get around. Be prepared to share these other options for transportation with them. Research on-line the numerous types of transportation alternatives for the elderly. If you are not able to transport them, maybe you could rely on a neighbor or relative.

Bear in mind the diagnosis of dementia does not necessarily mean someone cannot drive. This is a case-by-case decision. Mom drove for a long time after we knew she was having difficulty with her memory. It was not until later when she became a danger to herself and others that we knew we had to make a decision regarding her driving.

If your loved one is open-minded to a driving test or a driving course, they will see their own inadequacies in driving. They might not be willing to accept this, but at least it will not be you who points out their possible inadequacies. They may be more receptive to the idea of not driving if the idea comes from an outside person, not a relative.

Be sure to make them aware most insurance companies give discounts for taking driver education courses. Maybe they could benefit from a refresher course. They might be more open to this idea if you offer to take the course with them.

If your family member has been diagnosed with dementia and is still able to drive, make their insurance company aware of the diagnosis. There are driving lessons designed specifically for aging adults. There is information on-line regarding driving tests and courses for the elderly.

Should your loved one be resistant to handing over their keys, attempt to help them recognize the reason it may be necessary. Explain they would have less stress, as it is extremely stressful driving in today's world. In fact, you have possibly heard them complain about the stress of driving. Tell them if they would allow their friends and family to be their transportation, they would be able to see them more often. They could bake their friend a cake or make them a card to return the favor.

Explain the cost of owning a vehicle, upkeep and insurance. They will save money by not being out that expense. Explain to them they will not have to worry about injuring themselves or others if they stop driving. Be gentle when discussing your loved one's driving abilities with them as this is one of the symbols of independence they lose.

Their physician may be better able to tackle this subject with them. They may see an outside person such as their doctor as a more logical person to make this decision instead of their family members. They may trust their physician more and decide their physician is more knowledgeable about the subject of whether or not they should drive. Or the Department of Motor Vehicles might be willing to do an assessment.

When my mother lived with us, sometimes she would ask why she could not drive. I always told her I would drive because I knew where we were going, and it would be less stressful or troublesome for her if I did the driving. If I made it sound like I was doing something to help her, there was no resistance. Toward the end of Mom's independence, she did not like driving due to traffic and unfriendly drivers. Stressed her out too much.

Help them in and out of the car. Assist them with their seat belt. If they question what you are doing, tell them you are trying to make getting in and out of the car easy for them, which you are. I did this for Mom, and it made it so much easier for her. She was so appreciative.

Whether your loved one is able to live on their own or whether they are living in your home, caregiving is sure to become overwhelming at times. One tip I learned that saved time is to cook extra portions of food and freeze them, either in your freezer or in your loved one's freezer, for meals during the next two or three weeks. Make a large pot of stew on Sunday afternoon, freeze containers to have during the following two or three weeks. Defrost them from the freezer, heat it and you have your meal. It takes little effort to take a dish out of the freezer and microwave it.

This is an excellent way to keep informed of their caloric intake too. You want to make sure they do not overeat. Yet you want to make sure they eat enough. If there is a noticeable decrease in their appetite, this could be due to other possible undiagnosed health problems. You may need to check with their physician.

The sense of taste tends to diminish as we age. The elderly tend to put more salt or sugar on their food in an attempt to taste it. This can lead to other health issues. However, if the doctor says let them have sugar, let them. Putting weight on a frail elderly individual is usually not a concern. Fat reserves are far less as we get older. Again, ask the doctor about sugar. Avoid sugar if diabetes is an issue. Try a sugar substitute, only after checking with their doctor.

Mom was a frail 69 pounds when she came to our house. Her weight reached 89 pounds enjoying lots of chocolate shakes with Boost mixed in. Boost is a nutritional drink that provides protein, antioxidants, vitamins, minerals and calories. I am not sure my mom ever weighed over a hundred pounds in her life. So we were happy to see her put on weight with this regimen.

Help them avoid foods that cause constipation. If possible, be involved in the preparation of their meals. But let them help, as much as possible, during the preparation. There are various organizations that assist in meal preparation and even deliver the meals, such as Meals on Wheels.

Keep fruits, vegetables and healthy snacks full of fiber and protein on hand. At times, elderly people who live by themselves tend to not eat properly. They believe it is not worth the effort to cook for only one person. Or depression at times diminishes their desire to cook. They will likely eat better if there is someone to eat with them. While visiting them, suggest taking one of those dishes out of the freezer and have a meal together.

It is important to speak with your loved one's doctor regarding their diet and the proper foods to prepare for them. Oftentimes, the elderly have digestive issues and cannot process nutrients normally. If there is a lack of nutrients, the body may experience pain as well as digestive problems.

Elderly folks may not realize they are not getting enough water. You may need to make certain your loved one drinks plenty of water to stay hydrated. Nutrients need water to do their job. It also could help alleviate constipation, headaches, muscle cramps and lethargy. Water also helps keep electrolytes in check. If they do not like water, try fruit juice or vegetable juice. There are flavored waters on the market as well. Fruits and fresh vegetables are a good source for hydration. Cucumbers, tomatoes, bell peppers, watermelon, cantaloupe, oranges, apples. You may want to check with their doctor to be sure there are no fluid restrictions.

We could rarely get Mom to drink water. Her favorite drink was Dr. Pepper. The more advanced her illness became, she enjoyed it less. The only juice we could get her to drink was apple juice. You could take juice, freeze it and make it into Popsicles.

Not being able to function properly in the kitchen will bring more fear to your loved one that they are losing their independence. Reassure them you are working with them and will help them with options to make sure they are getting the proper nutrition, even if it means bringing in outside services. You could arrange a delivery schedule for a grocery store to deliver groceries right to your loved one's door.

People with dementia tend to leave food out and leave appliances on. If this is an issue in your loved one's home, put safety measures in place. You may need to post signs telling them to put food away or turn a certain appliance off when not in use. They may not like reminder signs at first, but after they forget numerous times, they will be glad there is something there to remind them.

Depending on the severity of their forgetfulness, it might be prudent to disable their stove altogether and have them use only the microwave or toaster oven. Install tamper-proof knobs on the stove, if necessary. Keep the appliances at the right height for them to operate easily and safely.

Have food, dishes, etcetera arranged at an easily accessible height to avoid injury while reaching. Explain to them you are trying to make it easy for them to retrieve whatever it is they need. Every time you visit your loved one's home, it is wise to check all appliances for functionality and safety.

I have found through research most elderly prefer to stay in their own home. Ask them if they would like to live in their own home for as long as possible. If they do, making their house safe and comfortable is imperative. Before employing any changes in their home, ask them respectfully if they are in agreement.

Your parents have lived their whole life with their belongings the way they want them in their home. It will not be easy for an outside person to come in making changes. They may become paranoid that people are trying to take their belongings or even their existence from them. It took some effort on my part to coax my mom into letting us make changes that would only benefit her.

Before you make changes to their home, be sure to let them know what you are doing and that it will make life much easier for them. Explain to them the reasoning behind the changes. Be sensitive to their needs and endeavor to incorporate the suggestions they make with the changes made in their home.

There are resources on-line to help with safety evaluations and what you can do to create a safe and healthy living environment. You will observe their capabilities change daily. Constant evaluation of their home environment is imperative.

Make their home safer by installing nonslip mats in the bathroom, by the tub, by the toilet, by the sink. Install grab bars on the outside of the tub as well as on the walls of the inside of the tub. Grab bars by the toilet area help with standing and sitting. Provide non-slip socks and encourage them to wear them.

Make certain all fixtures are tight on the wall in case someone grabs one in the event of a fall. If you are helping them bathe and they fall, try to remain calm. A stool or bench in the tub may help them experience less fear, especially if they have a problem with balance. For safety reasons, some caregivers replace glass shower doors with a shower curtain. Transfer benches assist with stability and help get the elderly in and out of the shower and tub. If you use a bench, the seat should be at the right height. There are walk-in showers and tubs on the market today as well. These tend to be a bit pricey but may be worth the price. The ideal situation would be to use a shower. Without remodeling, this may not be feasible in some homes. There are handheld shower nozzles available today that fit over the faucet for the tub. As this disease progresses, there may come a time where remodeling a bathroom could benefit everyone. If your loved one uses a wheelchair or walker, some doorways may need to be widened.

It could be beneficial to purchase a higher toilet seat to help with standing and sitting. Mom was only five feet tall, so it wasn't necessary for her. Sometimes people raise the entire toilet, if necessary.

As the disease progresses elderly folks tend to neglect their personal hygiene. They may dread taking baths and showers. It becomes a scary, monumental task for them. Noises are louder in bathrooms. Even walking has an echo. Be sensitive to their fears.

Water flowing from the faucet can be exasperating to them. When water is running in the sink or bathtub, we have to talk louder to be heard. Later in this disease, raised voices tend to agitate and scare your loved one. They interpret this as shouting.

Tape bath rugs to as much of the tile floor as possible. Fall mats are cushioned floor mats used on hard floors such as tile. These mats should be secured to the floor as well.

Be sure to monitor the temperature setting on their hot water heater. People with dementia sometimes lose the ability to determine temperature. There are devices that can be purchased which automatically turn off water if it gets too hot. They can be installed on the shower or the tub. If someone is able to still live alone, they are likely able to bathe on their own. It is prudent to use precautions anyway.

If feasible, use a mattress cover on their bed to protect from allergens. A softer mattress may be more comfortable for them. An egg crate on top of the mattress but under the bed covers could provide softness. However, keep the bed covers to a minimum. You might consider having a simple, soft down comforter for a cover. If you use sheets on the bed, make sure they are not patterned. This could inhibit their sleep. A solid, soothing color works best. Provide hypoallergenic bedding and be sure it is washed weekly in hot water. Dust mites rest on pillows. Use frequently washed, zippered pillow covers to cover bed pillows.

It is critical to keep bacteria and allergens at bay in their home as well as your own home. Sponges are riddled with bacteria. Wash sponges and cloths in hot water frequently. Some people throw sponges in the dishwasher for cleaning. Doorknobs and remote controls for electronics should be wiped frequently with antibacterial cloths. Vacuum cleaners have allergens, but they are effective in reducing airborne allergens. Studies show vacuums with HEPA filters are safest.

If your loved one is going to continue to have their own phone line, attempt to put them on every Do Not Call List you can find. Try lovingly to help them learn how to deal with callers who are trying to take advantage of the elderly, who are trying to scam the elderly. Mom received these types of calls almost daily.

In large print, post all phone numbers of those they may want to call. Or program everyone's phone numbers into your loved one's phone so all they have to do to call someone is to hit one button. In large print, post something on the wall next to the phone stating the name of the person the number corresponds to. It may be helpful to have a lighter phone as opposed to a darker phone. Also, purchase one with larger numbers.

Make sure there are carbon monoxide detectors and smoke detectors with working batteries in your loved one's home. If they are hard of hearing, there are detectors that flash or vibrate.

An option that may help them stay in their home longer is the installation of cameras. You will, of course, want to make them aware of the cameras. You can check on your loved one on your smartphone or on your home computer. If they believe this will help them stay in their home longer, they may agree to the installation of these granny cams. These are high-tech cameras, even alerting you to movement in their home.

Before the disease is too advanced, if your loved one is staying in their own home, it may be helpful for them if you make lists of what they need to do. Brush teeth, take bath, take medication, etcetera. Sometimes large wall calendars work better than lists. If they are adept at using the smartphone, they could write their own notes or record their own voice in their notes to use as reminders.

If they are having trouble remembering where items are, it might be beneficial to tape pictures on the cabinet of where a particular item is. For instance, a picture of toothpaste and a toothbrush, maybe a picture of a hairbrush on the front of the bathroom cabinet. You might be surprised how a small idea could help them not seem so lost.

Make sure there are automatic shutoffs on lamps, electric appliances, etcetera. Keep extension cords behind furniture or taped to the floor. Monitor this frequently. Do whatever you can to make life easier and less confusing for them. Again, the goal is to keep them independent as long as possible.

Whether they are going to continue to live at home or will be moving into your home, you will want to make certain all areas are well lit. As we age our senses do too. What looks bright to you might look dim to the elderly. Mom preferred to have a small nightlight on. Or she would leave the light in the bathroom on.

A motion light provides light in the middle of the night. Or try a touch light. Keep it simple for them to have light when they get out of bed. Bright lights may be annoying to them, but use higher wattage bulbs in the areas where they spend most of their waking time and in the areas that appear dim during the daytime.

<u>Dementia or Alzheimer's ?</u>

Elderly folks tend to spend most of their time in their bedroom. This is where they are most comfortable and safe. Help them arrange their belongings where they can easily access them. Perhaps an end table with all their necessities.

Mom would keep her television on 24 hours a day. It was bulky and heavy. My tiny Mom could not move it by herself. Having a flat-screen television could be hazardous as the elderly person might possibly injure themselves trying to move it. Secure any television with straps.

Try to keep clutter at bay in their home as well as on the outside of their home. We needed to constantly gather garden tools and various other things from the outside of Mom's house. These things could pose a great hazard and could also help a potential burglar gain entrance to the house. It may be advantageous to keep the bushes to a minimum as well. Check the locking mechanisms on doors and windows to make certain they are functioning properly. Stress the importance of keeping doors and windows locked, even if they are going out for only a short time. Also, as an extra precaution, it may be wise to install motion lights on the outside of the home, all around the home.

If possible, have a person do their yard work for them. Mom had a yard man scheduled to come weekly. She did not even need to call him. This arrangement is convenient for those who can no longer take care of their yard.

It might be beneficial to find someone trustworthy near their home who is a handyman and can be easily contacted. Post his number near the phone so your loved one can easily get in touch with him.

If there is a garage, take care that all precautions are used to make it safe. Label tools and all chemicals. It is prudent to remove chemicals altogether.

We were told by Mom's doctors depression can be a significant contributor to Alzheimer's or dementia. This is well-documented in literature on the subject. Depending on the advancement of the disease, exercise can help combat depression. Even with a modest amount of movement, exercise has been proven to improve flexibility, strength, balance and mobility. It could also alleviate joint pain. Basic stretching exercises provide benefit. These can be done while sitting in a chair. It has also been widely reported exercise improves sleep.

As the disease gets more advanced, slight exercise may also diminish nervousness and fidgeting as well as wandering during the night. Even a minimal amount of exercise or stretching could diminish the likelihood of a fall.

The only exercise Mom enjoyed was walking. When she was in the right frame of mind for a walk, we took it. There is nothing like sunshine and fresh air to improve a mood. Always consult with the doctor before engaging your loved one in exercises.

If they are agreeable, massages can alleviate muscle fatigue and weakness. Sometimes I would rub Mom's hands, feet, and lower legs. This seemed to be relaxing for her.

If your loved one is able to continue to live in their own home after the diagnosis of dementia, do what you can to keep them involved in social activities with others. It has been widely reported social disconnectedness is a major contributor of worsening health in seniors, especially those prone to the disease of dementia.

Encourage them not to isolate themselves. Studies show interaction with others may enhance mental as well as physical health. If Mom was in a pleasant frame of mind, she seemed to enjoy it when others were around, especially family.

The elderly may not have a large network of people to help them stay active or find ways to stay active. If possible, take it upon yourself to do this. Churches often have social gatherings, group meals and other events for the elderly. Some have transportation available. If your family member is able to volunteer, help them find positions. Volunteering is rewarding for the elderly, especially ones who have always had a desire to help others.

If your loved one still lives in their own home, propose a unique way to help them remember to take their medication. Maybe a medication chart or some type of small baskets to put their daily doses in. Another option is baggies. Put each daily dose in one baggie per day for seven days. It may be prudent to keep their meds with you if they are unable to keep track of taking their medication.

There are devices available that dispense medications and can be locked. They are connected to a call center. When it is time to take a medication, the user is alerted by the call center who will unlock the dispenser and dispense the proper meds in the right dosage. If the user does not take the meds out of the dispenser, the call center is alerted. They will alert a relative or loved one of a missed dose.

These monitored medication dispensers are available in a variety of prices with varying options. If necessary, devise a way your loved one cannot unplug or turn off this device. There are also devices that make an announcement when it is time for medication. As a precaution, it will not function if the medication is not taken. Google automatic pill dispenser or electronic pill dispenser on-line for more information.

Mom never wore one of the alert devices designed for the elderly, but I did research on the different types. There are devices elderly folks can wear called personal emergency response systems. These can be worn as a bracelet or a necklace. Make sure the clasp cannot be unfastened by the person wearing it.

The base station to these devices is connected to the home phone line. Someone can be connected to an operator at the push of a button. The operator can notify family members or neighbors of an emergency. Keep in mind these devices do not prevent wandering, they help to find the person who may be wandering. There are also wireless alert devices that do not require a landline.

Your loved one might consider carrying a cell phone with tracking capabilities. However, depending on the advancement of their disease, they may be averse to technology and would not agree to a cell phone. But it is an option. There are carrying cases for cell phones that can be worn around the neck.

There are also devices on the market with sensors built in to detect falls. They do not even require the push of a button. See Resources in the back of this book for a listing of Web sites that may help the elderly age in place longer.

In-home sensors is another option. This sophisticated technology will keep tabs on what your loved one is doing. Waking up, going to bed, eating, etcetera. The system notifies specific persons via text message, e-mail or phone of your loved one's movements. Advancement in technology allows our elderly parents and spouses to age in place much longer than in the past. Smartphone apps and high-tech computers, sensors, GPS capabilities and many more options are available. In the back of this book under References, I have listed various Web sites for products and services that may assist living one's final days at home.

If staying in their own home is an option for now, it might be wise to enroll them in the Alzheimer's Association Safe Return program. If they are found, the number on the ID jewelry they wear could bring them home safely. If possible, have remote care monitoring in their home so they can be immediately connected to help in case of an emergency.

Should a crisis arise, medical personnel will need to have access inside. It may be helpful and convenient to keep a spare key in a lockbox somewhere on the outside of the house in the event emergency personnel or family need to get in. You can let the local EMS know about the lockbox. They will put the combination in their database.

Make sure the outside of the house has adequate lighting including reflective numbers for the address so there will be no delay in EMS gaining entrance. Try to keep low-hanging tree limbs and shrubs trimmed so access is not impeded by bushes. At some point, EMS may need to get a stretcher into the house, so help your loved one keep clutter at bay.

If they have any physical limitations, alert the EMS personnel before there is an emergency. They will note on the address of the home if there are special circumstances, such as extremely overweight people.

It is wise to keep your loved one's medical records in a location EMS personnel can locate and have easy access to. Label the outside of the envelope or file so they will know what it is. If there is an emergency, they should not have to ruffle through drawers trying to find pertinent medical records. These records should be kept up-to-date, listing all medications, advance directives, etcetera.

If your loved one has been able to continue to live in their own home, the time may come where they need a caregiver to live with them. Attempt to help them see the need for a caregiver. Broach this subject with sensitivity and compassion. If at all possible, provide a consistent presence for them by having the same caregiver. A large number of different people around can provoke their agitation.

Maybe they would agree to hire someone to help them. If possible, let them have a say in who will be coming into their home to care for them. Approach this subject as gently as possible. They may have fears their home is being taken from them. Try not to be patronizing. Put yourself in their shoes. Frequently and lovingly remind them you are trying to help them remain independent and enjoy their home as long as possible.

Sometimes a trusted friend of theirs can help convince them to get outside help. The friend may be able to explain to them why they need to make the necessary changes. Their doctor may be a person who could urge them to accept help.

Keep in mind, your loved one could be resisting because they are confused. They may suspect their independence is all they have left. They may not appreciate that you are concerned for their well-being and safety. And they likely do not comprehend how difficult it is to maintain two homes, yours and theirs. Tell them you are the one who needs the extra help, not them. They may be more accepting of the idea.

Mom would not hear of an outside caregiver living in her home with her. She was resistant to any sort of help at all. She continued to declare her independence, even as we watched her slowly lose her grasp of self-sufficiency and memory.

If your family member is resistant to outside help and they pose a danger to themselves through neglect, Adult Protective Services may be able to intervene or assist you in how to handle your particular situation.

Working with a professional, reputable home-care agency brings peace of mind to you and your loved one. They provide compassionate and skilled caregivers who provide hands-on, personal care. Most home-care agencies also have nurses on staff who provide greater levels of care such as medication and monitoring of vital signs. Have your list of questions ready as you inquire with different agencies or caregivers.

If you hire an outside caregiver to assist, it is prudent to check references, ask for a drug screen, perform a criminal background check. Communication is vital to have a successful relationship between the caregiver and family. Patience and excellent communication skills along with a positive attitude are important attributes of any caregiver.

Remember, this person will be taking care of your loved one, coming into their home and possibly your home. It is never easy for them to let an outside caregiver, a stranger, into their home. Perhaps you know a caregiver. It may be preferable to hire them.

For a brief period, we hired outside caregivers to come to our house several hours a day to help with Mom's care. She was truly angry, wanted no part of a stranger coming in. She was hostile and hateful to her caregivers. And had she known what she was doing and saying, her heart would have broken.

It is not uncommon for the person with this devastating illness to lash out, even abuse their caregivers. More times than not, however, the caregiver understands this and tolerates it, realizing it is part of the disease. Most caregivers recognize this behavior, the lashing out and the abuse, is borne out of fear, frustration and paranoia of the person they are caring for, all feelings which are part of this dreadful disease.

It is possible side effects of some of the medications they are taking could be causing this behavior. Check with their physician regarding a change in their medication if their behavior is too radical.

If you are seeking help from an outside caregiver, maybe you can find something your loved one has in common with them. The transition may be easier. Search for something that could form a bond. Maybe they have the same name. Maybe they both like to knit or draw. Is there a certain sport they both enjoy watching? The caregiver could remind them of someone they loved from their past, had affection for. Tell your loved one the caregiver reminds you of their sweet, loving, fun friend. They may be more accepting of the outside help. They will be spending a large amount of time together. Having a shared interest might make their time easier and more enjoyable. If you cannot find common ground, you may need to try a different caregiver.

Remind your loved one daily you are there for them, the caregiver is only there to help and assist you and your loved one. Reassurance could go a long way in alleviating the anxiety they feel. The ultimate goal is to help them experience security, love, being cared for.

Ask them their opinion of assisted living and/or nursing homes. This conversation is rarely easy and will likely be stressful for all involved. Tell them you are asking what they prefer in case the need arises in the future, that it is your desire to honor their wishes. If they are agreeable, take them to visit assisted living communities.

It might be advantageous for all if this subject is discussed early on, before a crisis arises. Speak about it in a positive light. Use non-threatening, pleasant words in a calm, cheerful voice. Use the word community rather than assisted living.

"Mom, these communities have many activities and interaction with other people."

They may not be accepting of the idea of visiting assisted living facilities. Perhaps ask them to go with you so you can initiate the preparation for the next phase of your own life. Tell them you want to research these places for yourself and you need their opinion. As they see some of these lovely places they may become more accepting. They could even decide one of the facilities looks like something they might be interested in.

Please keep in mind, this could be their final residence. They are likely aware of this. It is not easy to realize you are coming to the end of your life. Be understanding, sensitive and considerate when discussing this subject.

Keeping the lines of communication open with family, friends and healthcare workers can make a huge difference in the caregiver's life. Communicate with your family members, even if they are uninvolved. Keep them abreast of what is going on with your loved one, even if they do not seem concerned.

You will have loved ones who want to help and are excited to help but do not know what to do. Suggest ways they can assist you. Be specific. You are the one who has made the time and effort to be the primary caregiver, probably sacrificing much of your own life. Ask for help from them when you need it, and allow them to help in any way they offer. Ask them to relieve you occasionally.

Sometimes they are willing to assist you, sometimes not. If they are not willing to help, feelings of being abandoned by your family may arise. If you do not have high expectations, you will not be disappointed or hurt when they are unable or unwilling to help. It is important to keep your resentment at bay. Resentment is not beneficial for anyone, most of all you. Negative, harmful emotions could damage your own well-being and hinder you in your efforts to care for your loved one.

If there have been harmful struggles and battles among your family members, if old baggage is still present, these circumstances you find yourselves in may intensify your struggles, battles and old baggage. As a caregiver of someone with dementia, you will not have time to participate in family squabbles.

Accept that you cannot make someone do what you want them to do or what you believe they should do. Everyone is undoubtedly doing the best they can do or the best they know how to do with the situation that has presented itself to them. Again, be careful not to misplace whatever anger or indignation you may suffer towards family members. It is not the fault of your loved one who has this devastating disease.

People handle these situations entirely different. Some go above and beyond, others contribute nothing. Patience does not come natural for some people. Does not mean they are selfish or unloving. Does not mean they are not a decent, caring person. They likely recognize they would not be able to provide intense, quality care for a loved one. They may know nurturing is not a large part of their makeup. Be grateful they have the foresight to appreciate this in themselves.

Both the caregiver and the person being cared for need a support system, need to know they are loved, need to believe they are useful. More often than not, family members pitch in and make this caregiving effort a team effort. Family relationships could even become stronger during this trying time. Families grieve the loss of the person they once knew. Be prepared to experience a vast array of feelings over and over as your loved one slowly changes.

Grieving is different for every person. Your family may not grieve the way you do or the way you believe they should. Accept this fact and concentrate solely on your own grief and your own feelings. What is important to remember is your own integrity, your own sense of validation to yourself, knowing you have done your best to care for your loved one. Depending on the nature of your relationship with your loved one, you might have feelings of grief and loss to a much greater degree than your other family members.

As a caregiver, you may find yourself feeling defensive about the one you are caring for. Try not to let those feelings affect your relationships with other family members. It is pointless to argue. Your fragile loved one should not experience any hostility going on among family members.

Some family members may drift away. You cannot let that deter you from the goal, to provide compassionate care for your loved one. Ultimately, that is all that matters. What is important is what the person with this relentless disease needs and deserves from their family, not what their family needs from them.

If family members are not available to help, either physically or emotionally, there are others who are eager to help. Connect with the ones who are willing and able to share this journey of caregiving. There is a large comradeship among those who have endured the same pain and grief you are enduring. Rally around those people, let those people rally around you. You will forget about those who did not help. You will always remember those who did help, those who had your back, those who were unconditionally supportive.

6 CARE OF YOUR LOVED ONE AT YOUR HOME

Your loved one could eventually lose most if not all memory of their own possessions and home. With a heart full of compassion, you will want to help them in every way possible to remain independent, in the comfort of their own home for as long as possible.

However, if the time has come to move them to your home or another facility, keep at the forefront of your mind how difficult this must be for them. They are likely aware that if they move, they will never return to their own home, their own belongings, their own independence. They need your compassion and understanding, your patience, your unconditional love. This could make a huge difference in the way this move is accepted by them.

As their disease progresses, continue to experience closeness to the loved one you remember as well as the one they have become, the one sitting before you. Give yourself permission to grieve for what was, but remember what is. Find a way to build a new life with the person before you. If they are now in your home, it is incumbent on you to provide them with a safe, comfortable, quiet place they can spend time in.

When Mom reached the point in her disease where she could no longer live in her house, we left her phone connected for a period of time with a message saying someone will return a call as soon as possible. It gives you a chance to retrieve messages from callers and, in your own time, return those calls and inform people of your loved one's change of circumstances.

Mom lived in the upstairs portion of our home. When she first came, she could navigate the stairs on her own. However, we never let her without first being behind her as she was ascending the stairs or in front of her as she was descending the stairs. At the top of the stairs was a sliding door. We attached a small lock on the stair side of the door to keep her from tumbling down the stairs. Mom did not know the lock was there. When she could no longer traverse the stairs, my husband would carry her. Sometimes she enjoyed it when he carried her, giggling occasionally.

If your home has stairs, the railings should be sturdy and strong. The stairwell should be well lit. Another possibility for stairs would be installing a chairlift.

Many assisted living facilities have a room they call their retreat or quiet room, where they take residents to sit with them, hold their hand, play soft melodies and calm them. When I was doing research on assisted living, I recall one facility had soft white, fluffy carpeting on the walls and ceiling as well as the floor. Relaxing music was playing and a small waterfall was running.

If you have the space in your own home, decorate a quiet room where your loved one can find peace. At times, you may find peace for yourself taking a break in the quiet room. Mom's quiet space in our home was her bedroom. This is where she was most comfortable.

She enjoyed being downstairs with us when we could not be upstairs with her, and she enjoyed sitting in the quiet of our backyard. It was imperative for us to keep her life as simple as possible, as calm as possible.

Following are some different ways we tried to make Mom's new life something she could find some semblance of peace with. We tried to provide memories of her past days. We wanted to help her remember her life, her loved ones, her surroundings.

When you are trying to communicate with them or get a point across they do not understand, try singing what you are trying to say. Mom enjoyed hearing me hum a tune. Engaging this way is profoundly meaningful. They may sing a small number of words with you. Imagine the joy for them if you sing with them. Musictherapy.org is informative on this subject.

Evidence shows music can tap memories and reduce anxiety, pain, heart rate and blood pressure. It can help accelerate healing, boost learning, improve neurological disorders, speech and movement and increase social interaction. Also anytime agitation is present such as during mealtime, bathing, taking medication.

Elderly people tend to love to hear tunes from their past. Artists from Mom's past include Andy Williams, Frank Sinatra, Bing Crosby, Hank Williams. Find a station on the radio that plays the type of melodies they enjoy. You could also do on-line research for the songs of their younger years.

Hang soothing pictures that will personalize your loved one's living quarters. Soft-colored flowers, beautiful sunsets, small animals, paintings such as Thomas Kincaid, etcetera. Depending on the stage of the disease, hanging pictures may not be feasible. A severely malfunctioning brain could perceive the pictures as actual life.

If possible, paint the baseboards and walls the same color in their living quarters. This is less busy and less annoying than several different colors. Keep wallpaper solid in color. You may find old or antique decorations at estate sales. Record albums, eight track tapes, picture frames, etcetera. Look for old comic books to leave lying around, comic books that were popular when they were younger. I visited estate sales and bought older pictures from Mom's generation to hang. She seemed to enjoy looking at those.

If your loved one is able, keep them engaged in activities. This gives them something to look forward to. You may find it impossible to get them interested in any activity. Try initiating the activity yourself and ask them to join in. Read to them, paint with them, make jigsaw puzzles. Try storytelling, look at photo albums together, play musical instruments, scrapbooking. This can be highly stimulating for them as well as the caregiver. There are ideas for activities in craft stores. Vary the activities, if possible, to avoid boredom.

Were they a sports enthusiast in their younger days? Maybe they would enjoy a sporting event such as a soccer game or hockey game. It doesn't have to be a strenuous activity. Try going out for ice cream or a favorite restaurant. Picnics are pleasant and relaxing.

We would play Yahtzee with my mom. She did not remember how to play, but we acted as though we were playing. She loved it. Another activity fascinating and enjoyable for them is blowing Super Bubbles through wands. Initiate an activity yourself, as your loved one might lack the motivation to do so.

Look for activities similar to ones they may have enjoyed in the past, before they became ill. For example, if they were an artist, have coloring books and Crayolas on hand for them. The adult coloring books on the market now are ideal for carrying in your purse. If they had a career, look for activities which emulate their career. If they enjoyed sewing, they could possibly sew on buttons or hem a skirt. Maybe they collected dolls. Get some dolls they can dress and make pretty.

No matter how small or simple the activity, they will most likely get pleasure from it. Their attention span and time they are able to remain focused may or may not be diminished. I watched Mom get enjoyment and pleasure out of even the simplest activity. She had a bit of a problem with fidgeting. So keeping her hands busy seemed to help with that.

Another type of activity could be something as simple as watching television. Some of the older shows such as I Love Lucy, The Lone Ranger, Father Knows Best, The Honeymooners bring great memories. Find funny shows such as those in some form. Television, DVDs, VHS tapes.

Depending on the severity of your loved one's disease, they might enjoy being involved with certain blogs or chat groups for the elderly. Did they used to garden? You can find a blog or chat group about gardening. They might enjoy participating in the discussions. If a large, desktop computer is too much for them, try an iPad or smaller notebook. There are many free apps that are ideal games to keep one's mind stimulated.

Maybe your dad was an engineer or car mechanic or appliance repair person. You could provide a small, broken item he can take apart and put back together. He may have no idea how to repair it, but you are asking for his help which could go a long way in helping him believe he is useful and needed. And when he does repair the item, imagine the sense of accomplishment he will feel. Make an activity board of tools he can fiddle with. This not only stimulates his hand motion but could benefit his mental stimulation as well. You can make a Peg-Board activity out of a number of different items, depending on their interest.

Whatever activity they are involved in, try low-wattage bulbs or unscrew some bulbs to dim the area. A soft, low light is less frightening for them. Keep the lights on and close the blinds or curtains at nighttime to help relieve pacing or agitation. Overhead track lighting with a dimmer switch works well. As mentioned earlier, in the early stages of this disease bright lights are generally helpful for them. In the latter stages, bright lights will likely be annoying to them.

If your loved one has a special pillow or blanket, bring it from their home to your home. Maybe they have a special chair they enjoyed sitting in at their own home. Bring it to your home for their bedroom and position it in much the same way as it was at their home. Anything they love and adore the most in their home, bring it to your home. Try to keep their living quarters the same the entire time. Oftentimes, people do not adapt well to change. Victims of this disease have an even harder time adapting to change.

Be careful to keep loud noises to a minimum, as this could startle them or scare them and cause agitation. They experience panic and confusion with commotion and loud noise. Turn off the doorbell in the area they are staying in. Turn the volume low on phones in their area. Encourage them to keep the television volume low. They may interpret the people on the television as actual people and become agitated due to too much commotion. Even dolls and figurines could appear as people.

Delusions and hallucinations are common with this disease. Towards the end of Mom's illness, she believed the stuffed dog we had for her was barking. If you pushed its paw, it would bark. We joined with her in giggling at the barking dog. It brought my mom happiness and put a smile on her face.

In the middle to late stages, the disease takes a toll on the person's ability to communicate. They may be unable to find the right words, which might confuse you about what they are trying to say. Oftentimes it is easier for them if you say words for them instead of letting them struggle to find the word they are trying to say. In your communications with them, it could be helpful to be as specific as you possibly can.

This is different for each person. Mom would not mind at all if we helped her find the word she was looking for. We often did. There are others who say this is not beneficial because it only frustrates them. If they get frustrated because they cannot communicate their need or want, it might help to redirect the conversation to another subject for the moment. Possibly come back later to what they may have been trying to say.

Their thoughts get confused and garbled, so it is difficult for them to get out what they are trying to say. Go with it. Let them talk. They need you to listen. They can still communicate, only their reality is different. Give instructions one at a time. And try not to sound too bossy. Make communication a simple, pleasant experience, if possible. Mom would become extremely antsy if we did not choose our words wisely. Short and simple worked best for her.

Folks with this disease sometimes have problems processing the words you are using, which leaves them unsure of what you are trying to say. Work through what you are saying word by word. They may become scared due to not understanding.

Interrupting them will likely cause agitation. Correcting your loved one will only alienate them further. You might want to discreetly agree with whatever they say no matter how far-fetched it seems to you. If the dog on the picture is barking, you might comment about how sweet the dog is. It is your challenge to accept the new ways to communicate with the person suffering with this disease.

It could be less confusing for them if you ask them questions one at a time, and let them answer before moving on to another question. Mom would get extremely frustrated and confused if we asked her a question that required a lengthy response. Questions requiring a yes or a no answer are the best. Choices can be overpowering for them. I would not ask Mom what she wanted for lunch. I would ask her if she wanted a tuna sandwich for lunch.

In the malfunctioning brain of a person with dementia, they may not comprehend what they see or hear. In your communications, it might be easier for them if you are specific in what you say. *"Where is the pen?"* It could be frustrating for them if you say *"Where is it?"* As opposed to *"Did you enjoy your breakfast,"* say *"Did you enjoy your eggs and bacon for breakfast?"*

In your communication with them, attempt to speak slowly and clearly. Enunciate your words. Always speak with a soft, serene voice and appear relaxed when you speak. Confirm their feelings, whether you agree or not. Speak in short sentences and/or questions. Anything long and wordy could frustrate them.

Make sure they can hear you. Yet keep the tone of your voice low. If I spoke too loud with my mom, it scared her. Call them by their name every time you walk in the room or speak with them. Mom enjoyed it when others called her by her name. And she loved when we called her Mom on a daily basis.

Your loved one may recognize a person they see every day, but others who are not regular visitors such as extended family and friends might need to identify themselves.

Try to use precise, exact speech. Always positive. If you need to say something to them again, use the same tone of voice and the same simple words. If you change what you are saying, it could confuse them.

When they speak, let them speak as slowly as they need to. Their responses might be so slow it seems unnatural. Let them take their time. Wait as long as is needed. They are trying to be understood. Their malfunctioning brain is not allowing them to make sense of what they are trying to say, nor of what they hear you say. Keep yourself composed when trying to communicate with them. And move about them slowly, softly.

Your loved one could be frightened by quick, sudden jolts or movements.

As you stand or sit in front of them, attempt to keep eye contact and pay attention to what they are saying. If you look them in the eye when speaking with them, they may sense love and trust you. When I looked at Mom as we were chatting, I could sense a meaningful connection with her. She would look at me directly in the eyes as well.

Always face them in a relaxed position. If possible, be at the same height they are when you talk to them. If they are in a wheelchair, kneel to their level. If they are standing when speaking with you, stand with them. If they are in bed, sit on the edge of the bed while talking with them. These gestures may help them experience more comfort, more relaxation, more loved.

When they ask you something over and over, answer them again. Saying *"I told you that a second ago"* will only exacerbate their fear of being lost. There will come a time when they will not remember something from one minute to the next minute, from one instant to the next instant. Remember they are not purposefully being obstinate. It is their dementing illness limiting their capacity to reason. When they repeat something over and over, have patience. The day is coming when they may not even be able to talk. Let them talk now.

Whatever your loved one says to you, validate what they say, if it is within reason. Accept it even if it makes no sense. It is their reality. Learn to make it yours. It is futile to try to drag them into your reality. Bring yourself into their reality and accept it for what it is. If they had oatmeal for breakfast but they say they enjoyed the eggs they had for breakfast, go with it. Tell them you enjoyed yours too.

There will be times when true reality is important, but choose those times wisely. It could turn into a battle. You will need to pick those battles carefully. I never had a battle with Mom, but it took me a while to learn to accept her reality.

Trying to explain why they need to do something a certain way will likely frustrate them. Let them do it their way, if it's safe, and change the subject to something else. If they do something wrong, it is important not to yell at them or shame them. No need to correct them, they may not remember. What they need is reassurance. Scolding, arguing or attempting to reason with them is counterproductive. Have compassion. You could possibly divert their attention to something more pleasant.

Rather than using the word remember in your conversations with them, attempt to help them understand what it is you are trying to get them to do. Take a bath, get dressed, eat, watch television. Try reminiscing about what it's like to take a bath or what it's like to get dressed. By reminiscing, it may trigger a memory for them of what something is like. But never force them to remember. Sometimes mirroring what you want them to do assists them in understanding. Take a hair brush and brush your own hair while telling your mom it is time to brush hers. Reminisce with her about brushing each other's hair as you were growing up. Mom and I did this frequently. We enjoyed it.

As their disease progresses, they may be unable to speak. Though they cannot speak, remember they feel. You could be the only emotional support they have. You could be the only advocate they have. You must be the best advocate you can be for your ill family member. Try to find creative ways to help them express their feelings. Within a short period of time, you will be able to figure out what upsets them, what makes them seem better. If you see them lose a train of thought, keep talking to them.

When Mom lived with us and her communication became difficult, we found labeling helped her understand. We had a "bathroom" sign, a "flush toilet" sign, etcetera. We found if we labeled how to do some things, she was less confused. The labels did not seem to bother her.

We used one of the large white boards to write Mom messages and notes of what we were trying to help her remember. We also kept a wall calendar hanging and marked off the days as they would come and go. This helped her seem a bit less lost. She would not have known what day it was without the calendar.

Always smile when you walk into the area where they are. Even if you do not have the inclination, give them the universal sign the whole world knows, a smile. If possible and when appropriate, incorporate humor in your communications. If you have found a word or some action that brings out their laughter, say it or do it frequently. Even the most mundane action you perform, do it if it brings laughter to them. Tell them frequently you love them.

Eventually words will elude them. Try art therapy. Let them use their hands and eyes to create imaginative paintings. If they put red dots on a paper, help them form it into a bouquet of flowers. You might be surprised at how your loved one can spend hours talking about a watercolor drawing they have done.

You can help them replicate past experiences with their art. They may attempt drawings or paintings of past memories, objects from their early adulthood. Did they crochet or knit? Maybe they are drawing one of the items they crocheted years ago but you can't exactly recognize it. Did they sing? Maybe they are drawing musical notes. Did they farm? Maybe they are drawing farm animals. Initiate exploring with them, engaging them in this activity.

Even discussing paintings done by others is a way to interact. Sometimes something sparks long-forgotten memories. Letting them put their thoughts on paper in the form of artwork is a way to help you appreciate or gain insight as to where they are at in their mind. Encourage them to draw anything they want. Creativity is still there. Help them develop it.

Experts say challenging your loved one with a new activity, a new skill such as painting, coloring, etcetera may help in delaying the progress of Alzheimer's.

If your loved one fumbles around in cabinets, it would be prudent to put safety locks on them. Childproof any cabinet they should not be in. Put empty containers in one set of cabinets without a lock. This will give them a cabinet to rummage through.

If they are able, let them help you with chores around the house. Cook together, go to the store together, have meals together. When cooking is done together, whether at their house or your house, keep the handles of the pans turned in toward the center. There are devices available for purchase that automatically turn off stovetops and ovens if they are left on. Whether it be cooking or sitting in the garden area, suggest ways to engage with them. They may be lonely and not know how to combat this.

Whatever you can do to help them feel they are needed could potentially add meaning to their life. Work in the yard or garden together. Always keep an eye on them in the yard as there might be uneven ground or cracks in concrete. All yard furniture should be secure. Take walks with them. Hold their hand if they will let you. We all have an innate desire for human contact. Stroke their hair, pat their arm, rub their neck. When I would brush Mom's hair, she would sit there with her eyes closed. I could tell she did not want me to stop.

It is imperative for them to experience security right now. Carrying something in their hand is a form of security. Maybe a flower, a paper cup of water, something to snack on. They might enjoy having a stuffed animal they could hold. There may be a memento from their childhood that would bring them security simply by looking at it or holding it. Try different items to learn what provides them the sense of security they desperately need. We had a number of stuffed animals for Mom.

Provide a rocking chair in their bedroom. The motion of rocking is sometimes comforting. Try to provide a soothing, inviting place in their living quarters. This might help allay pacing. Have several drawers of clothes they can rummage through. If they are pacing, a small table where they could do any basic activity such as folding loads of clothes may provide hours of contentment for them.

Remember to keep their area clear of clutter. It is wise to keep irreplaceable breakables put away or in a locked cabinet. If they get broken, your loved one might panic and experience even more despair.

Agitation behavior is prevalent in the life of victims of dementia and Alzheimer's. You may not notice their agitation in the beginning. It is not uncommon at all for someone to be opposite of the way they were before they were diagnosed. If they were loving and gentle before, they could be the total opposite now.

As the disease of Alzheimer's progresses, their agitation behavior may become more readily noticeable. You might notice them babbling or raising their voice more often. You might notice cursing and abusive language they would never have engaged in before. You may even notice physical aggression that was never present. I found when I ignored Mom's agitated behavior it made it worse. I learned to search for what was bothering her. More times than not we would find the culprit.

They are most likely trying to communicate a need to you. It could be stress related. It is incumbent upon the caregiver to attempt to learn what your loved one is trying to communicate. Use your own senses to identify what is causing the agitation behavior. If you can learn what the triggers are for the behavior, you are one step closer to alleviating it.

Redirecting the conversation works to diminish their agitation. If you see they are getting frustrated, tell them you need to go to the rest room, you will be right back. When you walk back in in two or three minutes, they will likely not recall why they were agitated before your rest room break.

"Mom, let's go eat some pancakes."

She was not ready to go eat pancakes. And they may not be ready to go eat breakfast. It is futile to argue with them or belittle them. Arguing will get you nowhere. Perhaps it is best to stop whatever is agitating them and come back to it later. Or turn it into a positive experience, if possible. Sometimes you will have to see things from their perspective.

If they are agitated, what was happening right before the agitation? Maybe you can identify what is bringing on the behavior they are exhibiting. Use your own senses to figure out the environment that is theirs now. If necessary, keep records or logs of this so in the future you will be able to know the triggers to avoid. In my experience with Mom, I found right after lunchtime was her best time. She was usually calm and at peace during this time of the day.

I tried to keep a log of what I considered might be causing Mom's agitation. If I saw a dramatic change in her mood, I would make a notation of what we were doing in the time right before the behavior commenced. Are their clothes okay? Are they hungry or thirsty? We kept a small refrigerator in Mom's room so she could get something to drink or snack on. Plastic containers work best. Snacks included items she could open on her own such as cheese sticks or yogurt.

Maybe they are agitated because they need to use the restroom and do not know how to communicate this. Maybe they are merely having a lousy day, like we all have at times. Fatigue could be a cause. Suggest a nap. Or take a nap with them. If they take a nap during the day, attempt to entice them to rest in a comfortable chair or on top of the bed, not in the bed. They may perceive it as nighttime if they are entirely in bed.

Sometimes a change in routine or environment is a contributing factor to agitation. Anything out of the ordinary could bring on agitation and anxiety. As much as possible, keep their current routine activities like their past routine activities. If they enjoyed reading the newspaper before, provide them with a newspaper now. Attempt to help them enjoy the same activities every day and do them at the same time every day.

However, if a certain routine is not working, change it. You will have to be flexible. If eating breakfast does not work at 8:00 a.m., try changing it to 10:00 a.m. If bath time does not work at 7:00 p.m., try changing it to 9:00 p.m. Once a routine is established, everything will go much more smoothly for the impaired person as well as the caregiver.

Always approach your loved one slowly and lovingly. If they are at the point where they do not know you, tell them who you are and why you are there. Every single time you see them, tell them who you are. Even before they get to this stage, remember to always mention the time of the day and day of the week. This may help them be more in touch with reality.

If your loved one engages in inappropriate behavior, such as sexual innuendos, usually the best course of action is to make an attempt to distract them. Get their mind off of what they are talking about. Next, try to ignore it. This is not them, it is their sickness. They likely do not comprehend what they are saying.

Mom never engaged in this type of behavior, so we have no experience in how to handle it. However, I have spoken with other caregivers who had this issue with their loved one. If you are able to remember this disease causes confusion and frustration in your loved one, you will be better able to cope with inappropriate behavior.

Oftentimes, elderly folks lose their sense of smell and sense of taste. They may experience a dramatic decrease in their appetite level. When you cook, you may want to add seasonings, garnishes, marinades, fruity sauces, etcetera to their food. You will want to check with their doctor to make certain the spices and seasonings are appropriate for their diet.

Problems with swallowing can sometimes be a source of discomfort. Oftentimes elderly folks enjoy smoothies. Nutrients can be added to smoothies. If your loved one had favorite fruits or vegetables in the past, these make terrific smoothies and provide great nutrients.

Some medications cause a loss of appetite. Check with their physician to see if this is a possibility. If they appear to have difficulty chewing, check their teeth and gums for possible irritation. Or dentures may need to be adjusted. Check with the dentist.

Mom never got to the point where she did not know how to eat. But as this disease progresses, some might forget how to eat. If they get messy, let them. It is simple to clean the mess when they are finished. Maybe help them with holding their silverware or show them how to chew their food. If they are having trouble holding their fork or spoon, try wrapping a rubber band around the handle. This gives them something to grip. This idea works with anything that might be slippery for them.

Sometimes elderly folks will refuse to eat no matter what you try. Mom would only ingest chocolate malts and shakes at this time. I mentioned in the previous chapter, we would purchase Boost and load the shakes with it, providing her with much better nourishment. You could do this with any medication in liquid form. You could also mix medication in ice cream, pudding, anything they enjoy eating. Some medication in pill form may be too large. Chop it into small pieces, put it in pudding. At the doctor's suggestion, we also gave Mom a crushed multivitamin every day.

If they are reluctant to take their meds, try letting them know a chocolate chip cookie or banana or whatever they like is waiting for them after they take their meds. Most people love to hear what an excellent job they are doing. Let them know you appreciate them taking their meds.

It is sometimes helpful to call their meds vitamins. They may be more apt to take a "vitamin" that is keeping them healthy as opposed to a "medication." It could be helpful to take their meds out of the original pill containers. They may be more willing to take their meds if it does not look like they came from a prescription container. We found this to be true with Mom. You will want to

127

be certain to label whatever container the meds are in with the name of the med.

Sometimes it works to divert their attention. Have a glass of water sitting there. Talk about something entirely different while handing them the pills as you're talking. They may grab the glass without even focusing on it and take the meds. This worked often with Mom.

Make mealtime as simple and serene as possible. If it is a battle to get them to eat, forcing the issue could exacerbate their unwillingness to eat and cause them to eat even less. This was a concern we had with Mom. So we cut her food into small pieces and sprinkled a tiny bit of sugar on it. She frequently used her fork to pick at her food but seemed to eat better when we left her alone and remained calm.

If feasible, use only the portions of food they will eat and only the silverware they will need. Plastic dishes and plastic silverware may be safer for them. Spices on the table could confuse them.

As this disease progresses, you may need to purchase some of the adult size bibs. You will likely need to cut their food into tiny pieces for them. Use a plate with a lip or use a bowl to keep them from sliding their food off onto the table. It is less confusing for them to put one item at a time on their plate. Remind them to chew slowly and swallow their food. My mother eventually did not know what to do at the table. We showed her, every time.

Brightly-colored patterns for napkins or tablecloths may confuse them. For example, they could perceive flowers on the tablecloth as actual flowers. Use solid color dishes, preferably soft colors, such as pastels.

Try to plan simple activities in the late afternoon to help occupy their mind and keep them alert until bedtime. If your loved one wants to wander around, let them. It may help to diminish their stress level and energy level in the evening. If the yard is fenced, they might enjoy wandering around in the yard. When Mom was able, we would go on walks on our street. Our street has seven houses on it, so the traffic is minimal. If walking is an option for you, an area where there is little to no traffic is less stressful for your loved one.

They eventually may pace in the late afternoon or at nighttime. It does not always occur in the evening, but most often this is the time of day it affects loved ones with this disease. This is referred to as Sundowner's Syndrome.

It must be terribly exhausting to be confused and sad, wandering around trying to make sense with what is going on in your life. This confusion damages the sleep/wake cycle and more commonly occurs in the middle to late stages of this disease. I've known caregivers who use a baby monitor to keep a close watch on their loved one when Sundowner's is present.

If this pacing is present, try to journal what is occurring during this time period. What do you see or hear just before the pacing begins? You could discover triggers for the pacing. And if you need to discuss this with their doctor, you likely will not remember everything if you do not document it. Their doctor may prescribe an antianxiety medication to help lessen pacing.

Hang a bell on the doors leading outside and install childproof doorknobs to prevent wandering outside. Round doorknobs are more difficult to open than lever doorknobs.

Alert your neighbors your father or mother is living in your home. They may help keep an eye out for outside wandering. It may help to deter your loved one from wandering outside if you paint the doors leading to the outside the same color as the wall so the door cannot easily be found. If you use a dark mat at the opening of doors, this may diminish wandering as the person might perceive it as a massive hole in the ground and not want to cross it. This is an idea I learned from a number of different caregivers.

Many homes have alarm systems that can be set from the inside so when a door is opened the alarm is set off. You can set these alarms for motion and door opening or solely for door opening. There are keypads on the market you enter a code into to get the door open. This is another option. This may take extra effort on the caregiver's part, but the number one goal is to keep your loved one safe.

They are likely to become agitated, distraught or nervous during pacing. Tell them where they are, they are safe and you are not leaving, you will be right with them. Calming music is at times comforting to them if they are pacing. It may help to sit with them for a time and have a glass of milk and a cracker. This may relax them and provide enough contentment for them to go right back to bed. Be careful with snacks containing sugar or caffeine as this could overstimulate them.

Many elderly folks have spent a lifetime praying. Perhaps they would be less agitated if you were to pray with them. They may prefer to have silent prayer but wish to have you with them anyway. Peace and contentment can be found in prayer.

If they want to go somewhere during the night, as sometimes happens with those who have no sense of time, have a reason you need to stay home. Keep in mind, it is difficult to reason with someone whose cognitive function is diminished.

As evening approaches, turn on the lights until bedtime to help keep them alert. Mom would become agitated when she knew the sun was setting. She did not like the dark at all. We would close the curtains but leave several lamps on to keep it well lit. If you close the curtains and blinds before the sun goes down, this may relax them enough to alleviate pacing. Keep the area they sleep in peaceful. They need a comfortable, secure environment.

It may be helpful to keep items such as keys, coats and umbrellas out of sight, as they tend to suggest it is time to leave. Bathing them right before bedtime might also over-stimulate them. You could make bath time early afternoon or morning.

All of these options may help your loved one sleep during the night. Try different ways to see which one works best for your particular situation. It may take some trial and error to figure out the best way to manage pacing. It is usually futile to try to get them to go back to sleep. This will likely cause frustration for you both. Sundowning can affect everyone in the house. Try as much as possible to minimize the effects.

Keep an open mind and be flexible when searching for a solution to Sundowning. Remember, no situation is exactly the same. What works for one caregiver may not work for another. You may find a nap improves the behavior of the confused person. Or you may find a nap will tend to disorient them.

Mom would nap several minutes at a time. Though she would be a bit disoriented when she woke, I sensed she was more alert after dozing. If they nap, strive to keep their naps to 20 or 30 minutes at a time, spaced out during the day. This may help with their inability to sleep at night. Some assisted living facilities keep the residents busy with activities during the day which means less napping during the day and more peaceful rest at night.

Before attributing pacing to their disease, you might want to rule out other health issues, such as a urinary tract infection. Some caregivers have documented certain medications, especially anti-depressants, provide some relief from pacing.

Sometimes simply sitting with them holding their hand will bring them peace. Certain scents, especially lavender, can be comforting. Try oil lamps or a diffuser. Soothing music is sometimes an excellent remedy for agitation. Choose songs familiar to your loved one, songs from their childhood, teens or when they were in their twenties. Mom enjoyed gospel music. Some television channels provide soothing music.

When you leave the house, it may be comforting for them if you set the stereo on a timer to play for as long as you will be gone. Play peaceful, calming melodies upon waking, more upbeat music in the daytime. Loud music could cause anxiety in their already confused world. My mom would get anxious and fidgety if the volume of the music was too loud.

The television noise could increase anxiety as well, especially police and crime shows. As time passes, they will likely forget how to turn the channels on the television or even how to turn the television on and off. If they prefer to listen to music, try headphones for yourself if you prefer to watch something on the television so you can still be with your loved one. Or put their music on an iPod with headphones for them. You may want to provide a narrated book for them while you watch a television show or while they are trying to go to sleep. Record a book in your voice for them to listen to. Your voice may be soothing for them and provide comfort for them.

Older movies tend to be calming for them. Put on a movie from their early years, provide them with a small snack, and you could see them relax while watching it. Mom was entranced by David Caruso from the show CSI Miami. She would watch that show every night it was on and say every night *"he's so pretty."* The show was on frequently back then. We do not know why he seemed to calm my mother, but it was nice to see her relax and watch a show she enjoyed.

Try a noise machine. These provide comforting sounds such as birds chirping or the soothing sound of waterfalls. Mom used to sit in our backyard for hours listening to the pool waterfall. She seemed so serene and at peace.

It is important to keep everyday needs sitting around, even if the bottles are empty. Your loved one needs familiarity around them. Everyday needs could include toothbrush, toothpaste, denture cleanser and fixative, shampoo, conditioner, body lotion, deodorant, electric razors (no regular razors), aftershave, perfume, make-up, fingernail polishes, slippers, Kleenex. We kept several of these items sitting in Mom's bathroom. I could sense it was familiar to her. Keep their environment feeling as much like home as possible.

Anything you can include regarding their past would be helpful. Older photos of family sitting around might help them maintain their identity. We would oftentimes look through Mom's photo albums with her. She enjoyed this but would become frustrated at not being able to remember. I would reassure her it was not necessary to remember it all.

Sometimes photos provoke a memory of an unpleasant situation. Mom was distraught because she could not remember my sister and brother who died at birth. She could not believe a mother could forget her own child. I explained to her a lot of time had passed and we all have difficulty remembering everything. I held her as she wept.

If your loved one has their own bedroom in your home, it may be important for it to be large enough to accommodate a wheelchair. If they are confined to a wheelchair, keep their clothes and other necessities at the right height for them to easily access.

Some elderly are prone to falling out of bed. You might consider shortening the legs on the bed. Or put their bed against a wall to keep them from falling out of the bed onto the floor. Also consider a soft mat on the floor next to the open side of the bed.

As the disease progresses, they may become shaky. Keep a chair in their bedroom where they can sit to get dressed, as fatigue will most likely be a daily issue. Help them purchase slip-on clothes, easy to wear items. I had a wraparound towel for my mother, the kind you might use at a pool. She loved it. Velcro kept it closed, so all she had to do was wrap it around her and push the Velcro. Her lower legs had a tendency to get cold, so I sewed another towel on the bottom hanging only to her ankles. Worked perfect.

If they have a large quantity of clothes in their closet, this could frustrate them. Keep the clothes simple. Elastic waistbands, slip-on shoes, large-necked tops, zippers in front or no zippers, no buttons. Pull-ons and pull-overs work best. If they dress strangely such as clothes not matching, best to let them dress the way they want to dress.

As this disease advances, you may have to get their clothes out for them and possibly even talk them through the process of getting dressed. In the latter stages of this disease, you will most likely need to dress them yourself. You may find they will only wear certain clothes. Let them. We had this issue with Mom. Buy several changes of the same item if they only want to wear certain items. Keep in mind your loved one is experiencing a gradual inability to grasp how much time has passed. They might think they recently put on the clothes they have already worn for two or more days.

Keep holidays as close to normal as possible. Holidays can be filled with sadness for the person with Alzheimer's. If the family gathering is at your house every year, keep it there. Your loved one needs to be surrounded with friends and family. Maybe even incorporate past traditions with current traditions, such as holiday music.

If your family member remembers older Christmas songs, sing them together. You can involve them in other activities such as gift wrapping, helping you prepare the meal. If they used to bake, let them help you bake cookies and cakes. If they had favorite decorations, incorporate those in your own decorations and place them where your loved one can easily enjoy seeing them.

I cook every holiday season at both Thanksgiving and Christmas. I wanted to involve Mom when she lived here, so she sat in the kitchen while I cooked. I solicited her opinion about how to prepare certain foods. I am confident she believed she was being helpful and needed. Anything you can do to help them feel they are useful, do it. Always involve them in family gatherings. It is your presence they long for. It is hurtful for them to be treated as though they are not there. When Mom was here, we never presumed she could not recognize what we were doing or saying.

If your loved one with this unrelenting disease has grandchildren or great-grandchildren, make attempts to keep the children involved in their life to some degree, especially if they had a close relationship before the illness. Help the children recognize the cycle of life. Answer their questions honestly. Toddlers may not even notice a sickness or a change. As children enter their teens, they will likely understand the effects of this disease and see their grandparent in a different light, slightly more fragile. Remind them to think of the happy memories.

Help them to know asking numerous questions to their grandparent could upset or confuse their grandparent. Keep the conversation lighthearted and simple. They may need to find new ways to have fun with them. Hopefully, they have been taught respect and patience when dealing with elderly. Oftentimes, adults shield their small children from elderly folks. But studies show grandparents need to experience hugs, kisses and touches from their grandchildren and grandchildren need to experience the love of a grandparent.

I mentioned pets in the chapter on caregiving. If your father or mother comes to live in your home, keep your pet if you have one. Those who suffer with Alzheimer's usually adore animals, even if they have never had a fondness for them in the past. Animals have a way of improving your mood. Sometimes even a person's appetite is made better by the mere presence of a furry friend. Most animals tend to provide love and comfort for older people.

As I mentioned earlier, my mom would walk around calling out my name. Through my research, I discovered this is called *shadowing*. Some call it clinging behavior. I have not seen an explanation for this phenomenon, but it is ever present in folks with this relentless disease. They usually desire to be around someone. This is, of course, not always possible.

Remember you are their lifeline to everything going on in their life. I had to force myself to let my sweet mother endlessly call my name. It broke my heart, but I knew this is part of this disease, a part I had to come to terms with through my tears.

Although I have not seen any explanation for this clinging behavior, it seemed to me Mom was trying to make sense of her confused existence, her overall confusion. Usually it is their caregiver who provides a sense of security for them, much like a mother does for her child. Reassure them over and over every day you will never leave them, you will always return, you will always be there for them. When I did this with Mom, she was calm. I could see the reassurance in her eyes.

You will not want them to think they are deserted, so if you leave, come up with inventive ways to show them when you will return. It might be a bit difficult because they have no sense of how long you've been gone. Something as simple as setting an actual timer they could watch may ease their apprehension. People with limited thinking and reasoning capacity have little sense of time. When you need to leave, it may be helpful to write a note stating when you will return. Always tell them you are leaving and, if possible, approximately how long you will be gone. Do this even if they are in the care of a caregiver.

As your loved one's disease progresses, check them frequently for feelings such as pain, constipation, a full bladder. You may need to ask them if they are hungry or thirsty. They may not know how to express they are thirsty. Just bring them water. Regularly monitor them for infections and skin irritations. Be sensitive if they are unable to express what they need or want.

Even if you believe they do not understand, always tell them, in simple terms, exactly what you are about to do. Mom usually was calm if I explained to her what was happening and why we were about to do something.

Have everything ready to go before you explain to them what you are about to do. For example, if it is bath time, have soap, shampoo and towel ready to go right after you tell them it is bath time. If you are going for a walk with them, get them ready and let them know right before you walk out the door. Each time you do something with them, help them comprehend what the two of you are about to do. If you have to delay any activity due to their refusal to participate, delay it. Try to keep them from being frustrated or nervous.

Take them to places they like to go. Park, church, driving in the country. If you are taking them out, prepare ahead so there is no rushing around. Rushing is a breeding ground for accidents and mistakes. When you do any activity with the brain-injured person, whether it be bathing, dressing, eating, you will need to allow more time to do it. They may have forgotten how to do any number of activities and will need your patient guidance.

If the activity they enjoy is riding around in the car, use the child safety locks if your car has them. In the advanced stages of Alzheimer's, the back seat may feel less frightening to them than the front. Mom enjoyed riding in the front seat.

They may not want to get out of the car. It is futile to argue with them. Drive around five more minutes, go back and try again. You may have to find some inventive ways to coax them out of the car.

If your loved one is living with you, you will likely need to assist them in bathing or showering. This is such a traumatic experience for them. Their brain sees bath time as total chaos. It is incumbent upon you to do whatever you can to minimize their angst and embarrassment. Sometimes your choice of words may agitate them. Instead of telling them it is time to take a bath, try telling them it is time to clean up, put on fresh clothes. Help them maintain their privacy and dignity by keeping a towel wrapped around them. Keep your voice low, almost to a whisper, as you assist.

Make certain the water is at a temperature pleasing to them. Be as gentle as possible, careful not to manhandle. If they are resistant to getting cleaned up, perhaps you could entice them by telling them you want to take them to their favorite park or favorite place to have lunch or dinner. Be sure to take them afterwards.

Daily bathing is not necessary. There are dry shampoos and soaps available that can be used between baths. When you assist them in the bathroom, get in and out as quickly as possible. If you are assisting them with bathing, attempt to keep their focus on you and your face or eyes. Talk to them and look them in the eye. This could help distract them from the dreaded experience of bath time.

It may be necessary to remove mirrors in the bathroom. Mirrors tend to cause agitation in those with dementia. They see themselves in the mirror and their brain may interpret it as other people.

When Mom first came to live with us, she was always cold, no matter how warm I got the water. I brought in a space heater and elevated it so the heat coming from the heater would be higher. Left the heater running for a period of time before her bath so it would be warm in the tub area when she bathed. It provided enough heat to where she was no longer freezing after her bath.

It is not uncommon for folks with this disease to become incontinent. There are disposables on the market these days that look like underwear. Your loved one may not know which one they are putting on, so you could replace all their underwear with the disposables. It may help to initiate taking them to the restroom periodically, if possible. This could alleviate the incontinence a bit. It may be advisable to install a toilet seat with handles attached to assist elderly folks when raising and lowering.

Mom never became incontinent. The weekend before she died, she was so weak we needed to assist her getting to the bathroom. She could barely function by this time, yet she knew when she needed to use the restroom.

If you are traveling, scout out the locations to make a stop. There is a free app called SitOrSquat that searches for toilet facilities. The app has filters that can help narrow your search. For example, whether or not it is handicap accessible.

Sometimes coughing and sneezing can worsen incontinence. As much as possible, avoid allergens such as smoke. People who are overweight sometimes have problems with incontinence as well. Plan ahead for how you will handle an accident due to incontinence.

If your loved one becomes incontinent, bathing them may become more of a challenge. Try giving them a sponge bath in bed. Keep them covered with a towel the entire time. None of us like to be exposed while being taken care of. There are no-rinse bath washes on the market. Many home health companies will send a home health aid to come in a few times a week to help with bathing.

If they are not incontinent but have slight lack of bladder control, keep a log of the times of day they go to the rest room. This will help predict future moments like this that could occur. You could even make it a routine to take them to the bathroom every couple of hours whether they need to go or not. In the more advanced stages of this disease, your only sign they need to use the restroom may be their squirming.

We could tell the change in floor from carpet in the bedroom to tile in the bathroom was perplexing to Mom. So we tried to keep it smooth using tape. If feasible, have the texture of the threshold going into the bathroom the same as the connecting room.

If you have rugs, carefully tape them to the floor all the way around the perimeter of the rug. There should be no loose carpeting and no bulges in the carpeting. It is prudent to have no throw rugs at all.

If your family member is living with you, they are likely to get to the point of needing round-the-clock nursing care. This may be the time to consider a nursing home. If your parents are still together, try not to separate them. Parents are sometimes resistant to nursing homes. When you speak with them about this, attempt to avoid the words "nursing home." Explain there are numerous options available and you want to work together with them to find the best option for the amount of assistance they need, yet still live the kind of life they want. If a nursing home is out of the question, consider the option of assisted living with nursing care. If you must place your father, mother or spouse in assisted living or a nursing home, make it as pleasant a transition as possible. Make your visits to the nursing home as pleasant as possible and visit frequently.

When my mom spent three months in assisted living, there were other residents who seldom had a visitor. Broke my heart when the other residents rarely saw a loved one. Even if they do nothing but sit there staring into space, they feel. Go sit with them, hold their hand, touch them. Let them experience your love. Aging is a road we are all traveling.

Even though your parent may not remember their visitors after they leave, they will remember while their visitors are there. If they react with anger or are unkind, remember they are reacting purely out of confusion.

Nursing homes and assisted living facilities provide relief from the stress of taking care of sick loved ones, the stress of handling decision-making for them. But the aspects of life that truly matter, love, security, kindness, those are still what we need to be providing to our loved ones.

Establishing a pleasant relationship and rapport with the staff may help ensure your loved one will receive excellent care. If something is amiss when you visit, try not to approach the staff in an accusatory way. You might alienate them.

Make your visits count. If you go with the attitude of wanting to instead of having to, your visits will take on a whole new meaning. If you are tense or anxious and do not want to be there, your beloved mother or father or spouse will sense this.

Your parents have loved you all your life. This will be your last journey together. Love them and see them through this last chapter of their life. You will have no regrets.

7 CARING FOR THE CAREGIVER

As important as caring for your loved one is the care of you. If you are not in excellent shape, you may not be able to help and assist your loved one. Too often, the caregiver's health is put on the back burner. Don't let this happen. Keep yourself healthy by taking care of your own physical, mental and emotional well-being. Should something unforeseen happen to you, you will need to have a back-up plan in place for your loved one's continued care.

As a caregiver of someone with dementia or Alzheimer's, you are much more likely to suffer from depression and illness. And you are the least likely to ask for help from others. Sometimes, we are unable to find comfort for ourselves through our family members, not due to us but due to them. They are unwilling or unable to grasp what is going on. Oftentimes, family members do not want to know what the relative with this treacherous disease is going through.

Join a support group. Most times, those folks in support groups have walked in the shoes you are walking in. If you believe you should be able to handle everything on your own, you are courting disaster. You are not in an isolating, helpless situation. There are tools available to assist you. Talking with others in your same situation will help you experience less loneliness as well as possibly providing other caregiving ideas and routines you had not considered.

It is crucial to remember you are not alone. No doubt you will, at times, suffer the depths of despair. While the role of caregiver is done by some of the most selfless people in the world, it is the beginning of a roller coaster of emotions for you. To the best of your ability, handle it with grace and dignity.

As a caregiver, it is common to have conflicting emotions. One minute you're angry, the next minute you're happy. One minute you do not know what to do, the next minute you have answers for everything. One minute you will want to cry, the next minute you will be laughing. That's okay. Your loved one is not the only one experiencing this illness, you are too. Let go of what is beyond your control so you can make responsible decisions about what is in your control.

Few of us expect to be caregivers. And when we take on this challenge, we are not aware of the magnitude of our quest to help our loved one. Nor do we fully recognize what lies ahead. We faced new challenges every day with Mom. We took them as they came and most times found solutions. My feelings and emotions vacillated daily from feeling like I could conquer anything to praying with tears flowing for guidance and strength.

Fear and confusion take over. You speculate how complex is this going to get? Your ultimate goal, however, is to make your sick loved one's life as pleasant and as simple as possible. There is no cure for Alzheimer's. You know what their destination is. Again, you are not alone. There are friends, relatives, neighbors and colleagues who are willing to support and listen to you.

Caregivers' responsibilities are 24 hours a day, seven days a week. It is hard work and is a vast array of emotions. The pressures will inevitably take their toll on the caregiver. Find a support network for yourself. The Family Caregiver Alliance provides a list of support groups. The National Family Caregivers Support Program is a resource for assistance as is the Corporation for National & Community Service. These Web sites are listed under Resources at the back of this book.

At times you will be stretched beyond your limits. You may experience an occasional panic attack. Your physical, emotional and financial abilities will be put to the test. You will experience helplessness and hopelessness. You may experience mood swings, headaches, insomnia. Remember, this too shall pass. If it is your parent who has this dementing illness, remember they brought you into this world, nourished you, cared for you, loved you. Do the same for them as they prepare to leave this life.

"You did good, Mom."

Words my son spoke to me the day my mother passed away.

"She's my mother."

That's the only rational response. That's all that mattered, she was my mother. We are commanded to honor our father and our mother. There are no conditions attached to that commandment.

You may avert burnout by keeping a close relationship with your other loved ones, friends and family. Continue, as much as possible, the activities you were in before dementia entered your loved one's life, and yours. Strive to keep your sleep patterns the same as they were before. Your energy level will fall short if you do not have peaceful, uninterrupted sleep. Statistics show caregivers often succumb to ill health at the end of caring for their loved one. Only if you care for yourself can you care for your loved one. If you are awake all night, you will likely not be able to sleep during the day either.

Keep your body and your brain active. Do aerobics, cardio exercises. Color in coloring books. Work puzzles. Read books. Write in a journal. Take a swim. Enjoy anything you have always enjoyed, especially those activities that keep your brain and body working.

Aim to get your heart pumping. Walk, jog, use the treadmill. Even 30 minutes three times a week is beneficial. Get the neurons in your brain working. If possible, take your loved one with you on a walk. When your heart is pumping, your brain is receiving more oxygen. Vary the exercise you get if you can. Doing the same activity repetitively means less neural activity. Walk one day, lift light weights the next day.

Make exercise fun for your loved one and for you. Your body will be taxed daily. Keep yourself in excellent physical condition for yourself and for the sake of your loved one.

Fall prevention is important when doing any kind of exercise. Move furniture, clear clutter, remove pets and rugs from the area. Also, make sure clothing is loose-fitting and the shoes have traction on the bottom. Use non-slip socks and slippers. And always have plenty of water available to replenish your body.

A trip to the park to watch the grandkids play is exercise. We all enjoy listening to the laughter of small children at play. There are senior fitness programs and activities available. Remaining active minimizes muscle weakness and stiffness.

It is vital to keep your brain working. If you go to the same store, vary your route. If you go to the doctor, vary the route every time you go. Take different scenic routes when you go out for a drive. Practice meditation, even if you have never tried it before. It is beneficial for the brain and beneficial for the soul. Experts maintain your brain is in better health if you meditate. Even 10 minutes a day can help alleviate depression and anxiety. As you meditate, your mind will wander. When it does, leave the outside thoughts and return to your meditation technique. You can search ways to meditate on-line.

Yoga can be good for the mind, body and soul. Caregivers tend to hold tension in their body. Yoga gives you an opportunity to release some of the physical and mental strain of caregiving. Again, even a few minutes a day could be beneficial to reduce stress and improve sleep.

It is cathartic to sit in silence. If you are a caregiver, this is some of the best medicine you will get for yourself, even if it is only five or 10 minutes a day. I frequently found myself sitting in silence. I hugged more often too. Hugging someone whenever you get a chance is also wonderful medicine.

There will be times when you will not want to get out of bed. Get up, take a shower, style your hair, do your nails. It is crucial to do whatever you can do to help yourself maintain some semblance of normalcy in your life as a caregiver. If you look and feel better, you will be better able to assist your loved one.

Self-talk can sometimes play a role in how you feel. Convincing yourself life is never going to be normal again, feeling sorry for yourself will only contribute to depression and anxiety. Make your inner dialogue positive. Repeat uplifting words to yourself. I am a great piano player, I am an excellent cook, I golf like a pro, I am so proud of myself for helping my loved one, I am so blessed, I will have some peace and tranquility in this journey.

Each morning when you wake up, make a to-do list and prioritize. When Mom lived with us, one of my lifesavers was my to-do list. Kept me focused on the task at hand and what needed to be done. Keep your goals realistic. If you have a large, overwhelming task on your list, divide it into small tasks. Or ask for help from a family member or neighbor. When someone does help you, show them your appreciation. They will be more likely to help in the future. We all like to be appreciated.

When caring for Mom, I found it difficult to multi-task. Try to focus on one task at a time. Concentrate on what is going on at the moment. You cannot go too fast. If you do, everything will seem much more complicated for the confused person who sees every action as complicated. Be patient with them. Rushing them will only frustrate them.

If your loved one lives with you, take a break away from them every single day, even if it is only thirty minutes. If feasible, take an entire day away every three or four weeks. Take time off to enjoy a hobby. If you do not have one, try to find one. Pursue it vigorously while you are the caregiver. I found my solace in piano playing and reading.

For your own mental and physical health, take a break from the responsibilities of caregiving. Your mind and body need to be rejuvenated. Do what you enjoy, whatever brings you excitement and joy, peace and comfort. Your life will go on after your loved one's ends. Be careful not to lose your own self in your valiant efforts to care for your loved one.

Understand your own limitations and be flexible. When you are able to take a break, focus on you. Do not let your mind be consumed with guilt or regret. Have a fun time and relax. You will be refreshed and ready to get back to the care of your loved one.

If you are able to take a vacation, have a family member or caregiver stay at your home while you are away. Prepare everything ahead of time so you can relax and not worry while you are gone. Make sure the house is stocked with toiletries and groceries. Have all the laundry done. Before you leave, you could prepare some meals to store in the freezer so all that is necessary is taking a dish from the freezer to the microwave. Meals on Wheels could assist while you are on your trip.

Let your neighbors know you will be gone and ask them to keep an eye out for your loved one and their caregiver. The purpose of your vacation is to take a break, unplug from your responsibilities and relax. Ask the caregiver and your neighbors to contact you only in an emergency. If your situation is such that you must speak to your loved one daily while you are out of town, try Skype or another social media. You might also consider mailing a postcard to them daily. It is important for all involved to be able to get in contact with you.

We took a short vacation when Mom lived with us. We came back rested, invigorated and ready to continue providing her with love and support and the best possible care we could. Chances are your loved one may enjoy a break from you as well. Bring back pictures of your trip to share with them. Be enthusiastic about being home.

Whether you are taking a day off or a week off, detaching mentally from your responsibilities of caregiving is vital for your own health. Taking this time off may keep you from developing burnout. It will provide you with energy to get back to the tasks at hand without resentment and frustration.

Medicare often will pay for respite care. In my research, I found medical insurance generally will not. Call local hospitals and request a respite from their hospice or palliative care department. Your friends and family will also likely be willing to give you a break. Or you can ask them to run errands for you. Church is another option to seek help. If you wait too long to ask for help, you could experience extreme mental and physical exhaustion.

If you are the type of person who is set in their ways, becoming a caregiver will undoubtedly change that. You will need to adapt to changes every day, if not every hour. Your self-discipline will be challenged frequently. Consistency is vital in someone who has this tortuous disease. Even though you will need to adapt to endless changes, keep your loved one's life as consistent as possible. When problems arise, take them one at a time and find a workable solution for everybody.

Spending time with other family members is also important. Spending time with your adult children and their families is important. Have fun with them like you did before you took on the monumental task of being caregiver. Involve them, if possible, in having fun and enjoyment with your ill loved one. Everyone involved may be able to traverse this journey with resiliency if a bit of humor is brought into it.

If you are unable to leave the house, call someone on the phone and have a conversation with them. Interact by e-mail and text, Facebook or any other type of social media. Invite friends or neighbors for a visit. It is important not to isolate yourself.

Perhaps you are not the primary caregiver of your family member who has this dementing illness, yet you want to help. You might be surprised how small gestures could help the caregiver. Run an errand for them. Help them with getting their children to and from school or other activities. Cook a meal, bring it to them, eat with them, and clean their kitchen. Do some grocery shopping for the caregiver. Maybe their laundry is overflowing or their yard needs mowing. Clean their house for them or arrange for another family member to do it. Is your sister the caregiver? How about a pedicure and manicure with her? Go see a movie together. Try anything you can to help ease the oftentimes overwhelming responsibility of caregiving. Use your imagination to consider what might ease the stress.

As this horrific disease progresses, there will come a time where a higher level of professional help is needed. You may be the caregiver for as long as your loved one does not need this more advanced care. Whether they remain in your home or a long-term facility, they still need your loving care daily. They need to experience your touch and affection.

There are a large number of options for extended care. I have outlined some of those in the following chapter. However, this arena is vast. Do your own research and find out what might be best for your loved one.

8 THE OPTIONS / TYPES OF HOUSING

Many years ago, there were limited choices for assistance with the care of our aging parents. You would hear about nursing homes, where the family member was often left feeling abandoned and forgotten. Today, options are limitless. Most people are not aware of all the options available. Keep in mind, as your loved one's disease progresses, the level of care needs will change.

If you are not a meticulous note taker, as you search through different options or alternatives for your loved one, ask for permission to record your conversation as you conduct consultations. Explain to them this will help you keep the facts straight and avoid the need to call back to ask the same questions over. I neglected to record any of my consultations. When I went back to my notes, I could not decipher my own scribbling as I was trying to write as fast as they were talking.

This is a highly emotional, confusing time for you. Most people who are willing to help you will not mind having their conversation with you recorded in order to make an already stressful situation easier. If you are not comfortable with this, there will likely be a wealth of information in the packet they will give you.

I am not aware of all avenues to finance home care. However, I have read about a number of possibilities. Help may be available through Medicare, Medicaid and veteran's assistance. There is a program through Medicare and Medicaid called PACE, Programs of All-Inclusive Care for the Elderly. This program is designed to provide coordinated care in the elder's home or in an assisted living facility. More information is available at Medicaid.gov and Medicare.gov.

There is a program called Aid and Attendance available for veterans. Also a program called Housebound may be able to assist veterans. Information on these programs can be found at benefits.va.gov.

Some health or long-term care insurance plans offer help. There are state and local programs that may offer assistance. Asset conversion is another possibility. Pensions, investments, IRAs or 401(k) plans. I have discovered through research that whole, term or universal life insurance policies may be converted into a long-term care benefit plan. Seek the assistance of a financial professional.

Research nursing homes far in advance of the time your loved one might need one. Contact your local ombudsman for help. If there are complaints made against a facility, the ombudsman should have this information.

Also visit nursing homes and assisted living facilities ahead of time, keeping in mind this could be your loved one's new home. Learn how the facility's typical day goes. To get a more accurate impression and opinion, do not announce your visit. When you narrow the search, visit again and again. This is the only true way to critique the facility and get a full picture of the surroundings and staff. How they interact with the residents is extremely important.

Visit a number of different facilities. Go at different times of the day. You may be able to glean a sense from your loved one of which place is more appealing to them if you take them to visit multiple times. If they are familiar with the facility and the routine at the facility ahead of moving in, they may be much more comfortable moving in. If you allow them to have a say in where they are about to live, there might be less resentment. Let them know that you want them to participate in the process.

Also let them have a say in what belongings they will be taking to the facility. Help them choose their meaningful possessions. Their favorite chair, their favorite photos. They may have an object that is a comfort object such as a blanket or stuffed animal they are attached to. Help them make their surroundings personal, warm, comfortable, familiar. Give them time to adjust, time to grieve, time to accept.

When they move to a nursing home or assisted living facility, use a Magic Marker to put their name on everything. Inventory what is brought into the room to be left. It is prudent to take pictures of the room and of your loved one frequently.

If you can't go by the nursing home daily, split the visits with your siblings or other relatives. Frequent visits by family members mean much better care. If there are visitors, leave enough time between visits for your loved one to rest, even if it is a short break. They may be more alert and ready for other visitors if they get a slight break between visits.

Request the nursing home provide the same caregiver daily, or as often as possible. When the nurse or aide gets to know the resident, better care is often the result.

Ask about your loved one's medications, who gives them, how much. Inquire about the doctor who oversees the nursing home, how often they come by, their credentials. Inquire about your loved one's care plan. Ask what happens in the event of an emergency. What steps are taken if your loved one is in pain? Find out what their policy is on family members hiring private aides to come to their facility to assist their loved one.

If the nursing home asks you to sign a binding arbitration agreement, consult with an attorney. You may be signing away your right to sue should anything untoward occur.

Geriatric Care Managers, usually licensed nursing or social workers who specialize in geriatrics, provide assistance to families in coordinating care for their loved one. They help to identify what is needed and find ways to meet those needs. Contact the National Association of Professional Geriatric Care Managers.

Senior placement or care management services assist in locating the right place for your loved one. They assess the situation and specific needs of all involved and recommend care plans and financial prospects.

There are people who provide services such as personal care, grooming, light housekeeping, meals and transportation. These services are called Sitter Services. They provide assistance at home or any other facility such as an assisted living facility.

Home care workers provide these services in the senior's home, usually when the senior cannot or will not leave their home. They sometimes live in the home with the loved one. These workers provide activities of daily living. Bathing, dressing, laundry, cooking. They provide companionship for loved ones, run errands. Some are licensed health care workers and are able to provide medical needs such as managing pain, providing physical therapy and wound care.

There are adult day care centers that provide day services such as rehabilitation or nursing care and meals. There is also interaction with others in these centers that elderly folks might not get at home. There are activities specifically suited for people with dementia. Your loved one returns home in the afternoon or evening. This service can be a lifesaver for the caregiver who needs a respite.

Day care is most often associated with children. When speaking with your loved one, it may be wise to refer to these adult day care centers by another name such as club or recreation center. When searching out these centers, keep your loved one's personality in mind. Are they outgoing or more withdrawn? Do they need privacy or enjoy people being around?

Residential homes are homes typically licensed by the state where the elderly live and receive assistance with all aspects of daily living. Residential care homes are customarily for non-medical care of the elderly. These homes are designed to be peaceful, calming and serene with family atmospheres. The ratio of caregiver to resident is appealing in these environments. They are in typical neighborhoods staffed by caregivers and/or nurses who live in the home and provide care to your loved one who lives in the home as well.

There are residential homes that are used solely for a day care to give caregivers a respite. These homes tend to suit some people more than the centers. There may be a garden to work in or kitchen to bake in. They are generally a more family style atmosphere. The following Web site provides information on this.

. www/agingcare.com/local/Adult-Day-Care

There are retirement communities that include assisted living as well as independent living. Nursing and/or health care is also available in some. These all-encompassing facilities are called Continuing Care Retirement Communities. The elderly may choose to live at a facility such as this in order to remain living independently for as long as possible. As their health declines, they are then moved to the assisted living part of the same community. Later to the part of the same facility that is skilled nursing. These facilities are ideal to minimize disruption in an elderly loved one's life.

Assisted living centers have the full spectrum of senior services for those who do not need 24 hour care. They have various plans designed to meet the individual needs of seniors and assist the family in providing their loved one freedom and independence while maintaining a high level of care. Many of these centers have a memory care area designed for those with increasing dementia. The area is separate from those who have no memory issues and provides 24-hour supervision.

In my research of assisting living facilities, I discovered they prefer to not have combative behavior from residents. Therefore, some elderly might not be accepted for a facility of this type due to their anger issues. Most assisted living facilities prefer calm, quiet, peace.

Nursing/Rehabilitation centers are licensed facilities that provide the senior with assistance in health care. They are expert in managing serious and complex or difficult medical issues.

Hospice care may be provided in the home or facility where the senior resides. These services include pain management and physical, emotional and spiritual support to folks who are in the last stages of a serious illness as well as to the family. Hospital beds may be brought into the home for the loved one's comfort. Hospice services specialize in end-of-life care and are generally covered by Medicare, Medicaid and most insurance. In researching hospice options, I discovered that many not-for-profit hospices will provide services regardless of someone's ability to pay.

Another option in looking for housing is to search your own particular state's options for assistance for the elderly. These organizations might be called Department of Aging Affairs, Department of Senior Affairs, Office for the Aging or Department of Elder Affairs. You should be able to find information on-line regarding different programs your state may offer.

9 CELEBRATE THE LIFE OF YOUR LOVED ONE

"What do people who are sick and dying talk about with the chaplain? Mostly they talk about their families, about their mothers and fathers, their sons and daughters. They talk about how they learned what love is and what it's not. They talk about the love they felt, and the love they gave. Often they talk about love they did not receive, or the love they did not know how to offer, the love they withheld, or the love they maybe never felt for the ones they should have loved unconditionally."
Kerry Egan, Hospice Chaplain in Massachusetts

There is always hope in the battle against the dreadful disease of Alzheimer's. New drugs are being tested and introduced into the treatment of dementia.

When Mom came to our home 10 months before her death, she did not know what a jigsaw puzzle was. Her doctor prescribed Namenda, a relatively new medication at the time. She soon commenced putting jigsaw puzzles together. I bought some of the children's puzzles with the large pieces. She improved from not knowing what to do with the pieces to putting them together quickly. She enjoyed seeing the final product of her work, a completed puzzle.

Mom's health declined quickly the last month of her life. She had refused to eat for months, receiving her nourishment from the malts and shakes with Boost mixed in them along with a small amount of food. She loved the shakes from Whataburger, so we would pull through the drive-through and purchase huge containers of shakes. We would separate them into smaller containers Mom would be able to hold and enjoy. She loved the big straws they gave us too.

In these types of circumstances, the decision must always be made whether to force your loved one to eat. The ideal situation would be if they made this choice before the disease progressed and documented their choice in a legal document. Mom made the decision and documented in her will, she did not want to be kept alive by artificial means. Force feeding? Was this "artificial?" We contemplated this, researched it and considered forcing our mother to take in nutrition by artificial means was against her wishes. For at least a month, the only nourishment Mom was getting was the shakes. My mom's tiny little body was slowly shutting down.

One of the caregivers who had assisted us for one day during the first three months of Mom's stay with us was a remarkable lady. She had the voice and the look of an Angel. I imagined she had a glow around her. Soft-spoken, gentle, loving lady. She took me in her arms at first sight and told me she was there to help. Of the ladies this particular caregiving company sent to us, this lady was my favorite. The moment I met her, I sensed she was a Godsend. However, we had her for only one day as she moved on to another company. I was sad our paths, in all probability, would never cross again.

Approximately nine months later, when Mom's body showed signs of shutting down, we called Hospice. To my total astonishment, when the Hospice nurse came to the door, it was none other but the remarkable lady with the voice and look of an Angel. Unbeknownst to us, she had gone to work with Hospice. Now my mom had this lovely lady to help her to the end. I wept. So grateful.

This lovely lady was having a difficult time getting respirations on Mom, but she was still clearly getting a heartbeat. My sister held Mom's hand, I held Mom's other hand. My husband had gone to the store and was minutes away when Mom's caregiver called him and told him to get home quickly. Within about two minutes of his arrival, the nurse lost Mom's heartbeat. I will always consider Mom was waiting on my husband to get back to the house.

So thankful my sister was there. She was so strong and talked Mom through the crossing over. She was so calm, so sweet, so tender with our mother, telling her it's okay. I knew it was time for Mom to go to Heaven.

As of that moment, my sister and I had been with both our father and our mother when they took their last breath. I cannot envision it being any other way. They brought me into this world, and at this moment, I could not imagine being anywhere except with them, helping them leave this world.

I have often contemplated what Mom would say if she knew of my efforts in this book to help others traveling this same journey. I suspect she would be happy, and proud. I watched my mom as she unselfishly and unendingly helped her parents as they aged. We told her years before her death we would be there to help her. We pray she recognized we kept our promise. I trust she knew.

If you have been the primary caregiver for your loved one, you have watched as they declined, little by little every day. Those relatives who were not around will say good-bye only one time. You have silently spoken good-bye to your loved one a little bit every day as they lost their ability ever so slowly to navigate life. This devastating illness takes away a small part of an individual day by day. Those small parts become big parts. It is a torturously slow, dehumanizing death. You have experienced the grief of death a little bit at a time every day.

Give yourself permission to grieve. There is no set time limit to get over grief. Sometimes it never ends, it is simply managed. You learn to live the new normal without your loved one. You may find journaling to be a source of healing. Try not to bury your grief. Don't hide the flowing tears. Allow yourself to go through it.

The journey of bereavement is unique to every person. You do not have to grieve the way someone else thinks you should. You have been through not only the traumatic experience of your loved one's death but the experience of taking care of them, helping them to the end of their earthly life. This day-to-day experience has ended, but the whole of the experience will stay with you forever.

You may struggle with a different kind of guilt now. You may be critical of yourself. Did I do enough? What could I have done differently? You are likely to experience a sense of relief now that the role of caregiver is over. I discovered from other caregivers that these feelings are not uncommon in this situation. I experienced all of these feelings and questioned myself frequently. Still today, I sometimes wish I had proceeded differently with issues that arose.

You may have guilt as you wrestle with the relief you might experience after your loved one is gone. From my own personal experience, I am convinced the feeling of relief stems from realizing the enormous burden of seeing our loved one in pain every day is gone, the excruciating burden of not being able to help them is gone and they are now at peace.

Feelings of frustration, possibly anger could arise now as siblings come together to discuss funeral arrangements or financial arrangements. There may be an estate to probate and take care of. It is not uncommon for tension to increase.

Regret may be yet another feeling in the forefront right now. Regret especially if you had a distant, strained relationship with your parent. You might feel as though you have been abandoned by your loved one. You may say how dare they get this despicable disease and leave me? How could they leave us with this to try to pick up the pieces? It is not unusual to have these feelings, nor is it selfish.

Celebrate the Life of Your Loved One

Write a letter remembering all the positive attributes, the fun times you have had with your parent or spouse. Write what was left unsaid. After writing, put the letter away, and when those feelings of anger or resentment rear their ugly heads, pull out your letter and read it. Having resentment in your heart is not only unhealthy, it controls your own life and could keep you from being happy.

While your courageous efforts may go unnoticed by some, you can be sure your loved one knew who unselfishly guided them through this heart-rending disease. I believe people who suffer this demeaning sickness can be aware of your love for them, your care and concern for them, even in their darkest days.

In this journey of grief, you have likely had an opportunity to learn about yourself. Think of how you have grown emotionally and spiritually. You are likely more sensitive. Perhaps your relationships with others have become enhanced. You have learned how to express your feelings and accept help and support from others. And you have provided help and support for others on this same road.

You may have discovered for the first time it is okay to shed tears. You have given yourself permission to experience all the vacillating feelings you have experienced during the duration of your loved one's illness. It is your turn to rest now and get on with the business of living an honorable and joyful life. Be proud in how you assisted your loved one, honored them by taking care of them, loved them and helped them to the end of their life with peace, grace and dignity.

Love is the common trait we all have, including our loved ones who have suffered this dehumanizing death. They sensed your pain and your tears. But most importantly, they experienced your unconditional love, your desire and willingness to help them, your unending devotion to them.

Mom may have assumed we would disagree on what she should wear for her burial. In her closet on a beautiful pink dress I found a note written by her. *"This will do just fine."* In her own sweet way, she made the decision for us.

The loss of my mother and father has left an empty space in my heart. But I celebrate their life now. I am grateful and feel blessed they were my parents. I can go to their gravesite without crying. I can look at pictures of them without tearing up. I am able to write this book without feeling sadness.

I smile when I remember my parents, the kind, caring, generous souls they were.

Through the countless mistakes my parents made, through the challenges my family faced as we were growing up, we always held my parents in high regard. Watching the courage and strength my mom exhibited in her lifetime, but especially during her illness, the dignity she held, still at times overwhelms me and I weep. If I can only get one more hug, one more I love you, if she could hold my face one more time.

Rest in peace, sweet little lady. You are no longer lost.

Mom did not keep a diary but would sometimes jot down her thoughts and feelings. The following pages are letters Mom wrote as she battled this dreadful disease.

younger generations will be worn out physically & mentally by the time they reach their early to mid-60's !! For they will not have the memories of a calm, peaceful, slow-paced life... — I ~~am~~ am so thankful that I can remember those wonderful, wonderful times — when people had time to ~~spare~~ spare and *real* time for each other.

Dementia or Alzheimer's ?

1-03

This ugly thing in my life seems to, at times, overwhelm me. I thought I would have more time. I did not know that "it" would so hard on the nerves! Maybe, just maybe, I am fighting it too hard! That may be quite possible for let me tell you — everything within me is yelling <u>No</u>, I refuse to give in to you! You try to fool me, for when I do make mistakes, you - ugly you try to tell me you are taking charge. Well, I tell you No! <u>No</u>, you will not make me lose my precious + wonderful memories and I'm here to tell you, I do not like what you are doing to my nerves so just move out + leave me alone !! I love the life that the Lord gave me and I know it was & was His intent that you be a part of my life so

184

- 2 -

get gone — and do not go to some
one else's life, they will hate you,
too!

X later

I seem to want to cry often and my
nerves seem to be out of control at
times — is this a part of your attack?
I think frustration has become my
middle name.

Yes, at times, it seems you are
so determined to overpower me and
at times, I almost give in but then
the best in me says No! You are
not a part of me + you do not
belong in my life.

I cry sometimes and feel frustrated,
my nerves seem to be on edge BUT
I realize that is a result of the
battle we are having against each
other!

Dementia or Alzheimer's ?

Getting older and not able to keep up things as I once could, has sure been a challenge - I get so frustrated with me! And now, ~~I~~ I have to also deal with you, you are a bitter enemy ..

4.03 My frustration with myself, at times overwhelms me! Seems like I really can't run the race of life but then why should I, at my age? I seem to not remember things at times so is that you or is it just age + lack of interest? Could be that the world runs so fast, my aging body + mind can no longer keep up with ALL things! Big ALL, for life in this time is absolutely too BUSY! - not just for me but for everyone. These

186

Thank you for allowing me to share my experience with you. My hope is that it encourages you and reminds you of how resilient you can be should you embark on a caregiving journey of your own.

If you would, please take a few minutes to leave a review for this book on Amazon.com

RobinGailWriter.com

10 RESOURCES

www.acrnet.org – Association for Conflict Resolution

Adult Protective Services – 1-800-252-5400

Ages and Disabled/Texas Department of Human Services – 817-321-8000

www.AgingCare.com/local/adult-day-care

Alzheimer's Association – 817-336-4949; helpline 800-272-3900

Alzheimer's Foundation of America helpline – 866-232-8484

www.alz.org/safereturn - 1-888-572-8566

American Association of Retired Person – www.aarp.org

Association for Frontotemporal Degeneration (AFTD) – 866-507-7222; www.theaftd.org

www.CareManager.org – 520-881-8008

Corporation for National & Community Service www.nationalservice.gov/programs/senior-corps/seniorcorps-programs/senior-companions

ElderCarelink.com connects you with eldercare providers

Eldercare.gov connects you to community services for the elderly

Resources

www.EldercareMediators.com – National Eldercare mediator network

Emergency Response/Lifeline – 888-877-4895

Federal Trade Commission – www.ftc.gov or 877-382-4357

Geriatric Care Managers are knowledgeable in insurance, Medicare and finding resources to assist caregivers. The National Association of Professional Care Managers can help you find a GCM in your area 520-881-8008, www.CareManager.org

www.GetPalliative Care.org

www.GrandCare.com – 262-338-6147

www.GreatCall.com – 800-733-6632

Hospice Association of America – 1-202-546-4759, www.hospice-america.org

Lewy Body Dementia Association - www.lbda.org

Lewy Body National Office – 404-935-6444

Lewy Body Caregiver Link – 800-539-9767

www.LifeLineSys.com – 800-380-3111

www.LTCOmbudsman.org

Medicare.gov, 1-800-MEDICARE (1-800-633-4227)

www.MobileHelpNow.com – 800-800-1710

Dementia or Alzheimer's ?

www.musictherapy.org

National Adult Day Services Association (NADSA) – 1-877-745-1440, www.nadsa.org

National Association of Professional Geriatric Care Managers 520-881-8008

National Family Caregivers Support Program www.aoa.acl.gov/AoA_Programs/HCLTC/caregiver

National Hospice and Palliative Care Organization (NHPCO) - 1-800-658-8898, www.nhpco.org

www.roadwisereview.com is a free program. The AARP has online courses. www.aarpdriversafety.org

SitOrSquat is a free app that locates restrooms when you are traveling

Texas Department of Protective and Regulatory Services, 1-800-252-5400 (adult abuse, neglect and financial exploitation)

Texas Department on Aging – 1-800-252-2412, www.tdoa.state.tx.us/elderite.htm

The Family Caregiver Alliance (800-445-8106, www.Caregiver.org) provides a list of support groups.

The National Fraud Information Center 800-876-7060

The Well Spouse Association – 800-838-0879, www.WellSpouse.org

Following are Web sites providing up-to-date information regarding technology to assist with aging in place.

www.mylively.com

www.connectamerica.com

www.grandcare.com

www.mobilehelpnow.com

www.reminder-rosie.com

www.medminder.com

www.lifeline.philips.com

www.medicalalertcomparison.com

www.lifealerthelp.com

10197813R00116

Made in the USA
Lexington, KY
19 September 2018